IT’S GONNA B[illegible]

☐ RIGHT NOW ☐ FAIRLY SOON ☐ EVENTUALLY

- ☐ It’ll grow back.
- ☐ You’ll get over it.
- ☐ You can do this.
- ☐ It wasn’t that obvious.
- ☐ This too shall pass.
- ☐ You’re too good for him.
- ☐ You’re too good for her.
- ☐ I’ll never tell.
- ☐ Don’t blame yourself.
- ☐ There are other fish in the sea.
- ☐ Tattoo removal is easier now.
- ☐ You are not your job.
- ☐ Your mother will never know.
- ☐ Nothing therapy won’t cure.
- ☐ Just take a mulligan.
- ☐ Moving home is no big deal.
- ☐ Don’t “should” all over yourself.
- ☐ At least you know you’re right.
- ☐ You did your best.
- ☐ Can’t win ’em all.
- ☐ You couldn’t have known.
- ☐ My cousin had that and was fine.
- ☐ Laughter is the best medicine.
- ☐ Have faith.
- ☐ Penicillin clears that up fast.
- ☐ He wasn’t thinking.
- ☐ She wasn’t thinking.
- ☐ If at first you don’t succeed . . .
- ☐ It’s about quality, not quantity.
- ☐ That’s not old, it’s vintage.
- ☐ You’re not old, you’re vintage.
- ☐ Things happen for a reason.
- ☐ It’ll look better in the morning.
- ☐ You can blog about it.
- ☐ We’ll look back later and laugh.
- ☐ No one will ever know.
- ☐ Here’s a hug.
- ☐ They don’t deserve you.
- ☐ Every cloud has a silver lining.
- ☐ It was totally his fault.
- ☐ It was totally her fault.
- ☐ A rising tide lifts all boats.
- ☐ There are specialists for that.
- ☐ Think of the big picture.
- ☐ Don’t let it bother you so much.
- ☐ No one saw you trip.
- ☐ You’ll get that promotion soon.
- ☐ It could’ve been much worse.
- ☐ Aim for the stars.
- ☐ You’ll forget about it, I promise.

- ☐ All publicity is good publicity.
- ☐ You can always return it.
- ☐ That was [illegible]derstandable.
- ☐ You look great.
- ☐ You look great for your [illegible]
- ☐ That happens to everyo[illegible]
- ☐ You made your point.
- ☐ Who wants that responsibility?
- ☐ It’s not more than you can handle.
- ☐ Time heals all wounds.
- ☐ Time wounds all heels.
- ☐ I’m sure you don’t normally do that.
- ☐ Success or not, you are loved.
- ☐ It’s a journey, not a destination.
- ☐ It was a long shot anyway.
- ☐ Lesson learned.
- ☐ It’s not you, it’s the economy.
- ☐ You can always sue.
- ☐ You’re the bigger person.
- ☐ You still have your honor.
- ☐ You still have your hair.
- ☐ Heartbreak makes you wiser.
- ☐ People will see through that.
- ☐ You’ll be the last one standing.
- ☐ Don’t let it get you down.
- ☐ It’s not forever.
- ☐ There are always people like that.
- ☐ Never fear, karma’s a bitch.
- ☐ I think it looks cute.
- ☐ One door closes, another opens.
- ☐ It’s all part of the plan.
- ☐ Go ahead, cry it out.
- ☐ They spelled your name right.
- ☐ Jobs come, jobs go.
- ☐ People come, people go.
- ☐ This must be hard for you.
- ☐ Time to get on with your life.
- ☐ Everyone’s a critic.
- ☐ It’s for the best.
- ☐ Don’t go there.
- ☐ It’s their loss.
- ☐ You can focus on your career.
- ☐ You can focus on your kids.
- ☐ Didn’t kill ya; made ya stronger.
- ☐ Ours is not to reason why.
- ☐ Don’t take it home with you.
- ☐ Timing is everything.
- ☐ You’ll eventually love it.
- ☐ Think positive.
- ☐ Think denial.

- ☐ Someday you’ll understand.
- ☐ Single life is actually better.
- ☐ Always darkest before the dawn.
- ☐ [illegible]browser history.
- [illegible]g.
- [illegible]t.
- [illegible] it.
- ☐ W[illegible]there’s a will . . .
- ☐ Chalk it up to experience.
- ☐ Cross that bridge later.
- ☐ One day at a time.
- ☐ You can always get it fixed.
- ☐ Don’t sweat the small stuff.
- ☐ Not over ’til the fat lady sings.
- ☐ It’s all nonsense anyway.
- ☐ You gotta believe in you.
- ☐ I believe in you.
- ☐ Anything is possible.
- ☐ You reacted with integrity.
- ☐ You can sell it online.
- ☐ Don’t get mad, get even.
- ☐ No one can tell it’s a knockoff.
- ☐ Just say no.
- ☐ Hang in there, baby.
- ☐ If it’s not one thing, it’s another.
- ☐ It’ll build character.
- ☐ It was meant to be.
- ☐ It wasn’t meant to be.
- ☐ If it’s meant to be, it’ll happen.
- ☐ Keep your chin up.
- ☐ You don’t need their approval.
- ☐ For every hill there’s a valley.
- ☐ I would’ve done the same.
- ☐ Life goes on.
- ☐ Absence makes love stronger.
- ☐ Can’t beat ’em? Join ’em.
- ☐ Shake it off.
- ☐ No one heard it.
- ☐ Better late than never.
- ☐ Better safe than sorry.
- ☐ And so it goes.
- ☐ The first cut is the deepest.
- ☐ Love hurts.
- ☐ Love stinks.
- ☐ Love is overrated.
- ☐ Soon this’ll be a distant memory.
- ☐ Keep on truckin’.
- ☐ Quit worrying.
- ☐ It’s water under the bridge.
- ☐ Don’t dwell on it.

- ☐ Ya gotta do what ya gotta do.
- ☐ When it rains, it pours.
- ☐ Every rose has a thorn.
- ☐ You gave it your best shot.
- ☐ There, there.
- ☐ It takes all kinds.
- ☐ They’re just jealous.
- ☐ It’ll come when you’re ready.
- ☐ Nobody mentioned it.
- ☐ Try to keep it in perspective.
- ☐ Put on your big girl panties.
- ☐ Put on your big boy briefs.
- ☐ There’s a lid for every pot.
- ☐ He’s probably out of town.
- ☐ Her phone is probably dead.
- ☐ You’re better off.
- ☐ It happens sometimes.
- ☐ They don’t understand you.
- ☐ It was an honest mistake.
- ☐ Money can’t buy love.
- ☐ Adversity forges character.
- ☐ You’ll feel better after a bath.
- ☐ You’ll feel better after a drink.
- ☐ It’ll make great memoir material.
- ☐ Quit blaming yourself.
- ☐ There’s no such thing as normal.
- ☐ You’ll show them.
- ☐ This will forge your character.
- ☐ You’re a superstar.
- ☐ Just explain what happened.
- ☐ Don’t compare.
- ☐ All parents screw up.
- ☐ All kids screw up.
- ☐ At least you have your health.
- ☐ He’ll grow out of it.
- ☐ She’ll grow out of it.
- ☐ Shhh. Shhh. It’s okay now.
- ☐ Pain is temporary.
- ☐ I agree with you.
- ☐ One day you’ll know why.
- ☐ You march to your own beat.
- ☐ Ignore what others think.
- ☐ Buck up, buckwheat.
- ☐ Everyone sympathizes.
- ☐ You’re overthinking this.
- ☐ Get back up on the horse.
- ☐ Just give it some time.
- ☐ It’s not the end of the world.
- ☐ It gets better.
- ☐ Really, it is.

☐ TOTALLY OKAY ☐ PRETTY OKAY ☐ OKAY-ISH

SIGNATURE	MONTH	DAY	YEAR

“OKAY? OKAY. OKAY!”

IT'S GONNA BE OKAY

☐ **RIGHT NOW** ☐ **FAIRLY SOON** ☐ **EVENTUALLY**

☐ It'll grow back.
☐ You'll get over it.
☐ You can do this.
☐ It wasn't that obvious.
☐ This too shall pass.
☐ You're too good for him.
☐ You're too good for her.
☐ I'll never tell.
☐ Don't blame yourself.
☐ There are other fish in the sea.
☐ Tattoo removal is easier now.
☐ You are not your job.
☐ Your mother will never know.
☐ Nothing therapy won't cure.
☐ Just take a mulligan.
☐ Moving home is no big deal.
☐ Don't "should" all over yourself.
☐ At least you know you're right.
☐ You did your best.
☐ Can't win 'em all.
☐ You couldn't have known.
☐ My cousin had that and was fine.
☐ Laughter is the best medicine.
☐ Have faith.
☐ Penicillin clears that up fast.
☐ He wasn't thinking.
☐ She wasn't thinking.
☐ If at first you don't succeed . . .
☐ It's about quality, not quantity.
☐ That's not old, it's vintage.
☐ You're not old, you're vintage.
☐ Things happen for a reason.
☐ It'll look better in the morning.
☐ You can blog about it.
☐ We'll look back later and laugh.
☐ No one will ever know.
☐ Here's a hug.
☐ They don't deserve you.
☐ Every cloud has a silver lining.
☐ It was totally his fault.
☐ It was totally her fault.
☐ A rising tide lifts all boats.
☐ There are specialists for that.
☐ Think of the big picture.
☐ Don't let it bother you so much.
☐ No one saw you trip.
☐ You'll get that promotion soon.
☐ It could've been much worse.
☐ Aim for the stars.
☐ You'll forget about it, I promise.

☐ All publicity is good publicity.
☐ You can always return it.
☐ That was so understandable.
☐ You look great.
☐ You look great for your age.
☐ That happens to everyone.
☐ You made your point.
☐ Who wants that responsibility?
☐ It's not more than you can handle.
☐ Time heals all wounds.
☐ Time wounds all heels.
☐ I'm sure you don't normally do that.
☐ Success or not, you are loved.
☐ It's a journey, not a destination.
☐ It was a long shot anyway.
☐ Lesson learned.
☐ It's not you, it's the economy.
☐ You can always sue.
☐ You're the bigger person.
☐ You still have your honor.
☐ You still have your hair.
☐ Heartbreak makes you wiser.
☐ People will see through that.
☐ You'll be the last one standing.
☐ Don't let it get you down.
☐ It's not forever.
☐ There are always people like that.
☐ Never fear, karma's a bitch.
☐ I think it looks cute.
☐ One door closes, another opens.
☐ It's all part of the plan.
☐ Go ahead, cry it out.
☐ They spelled your name right.
☐ Jobs come, jobs go.
☐ People come, people go.
☐ This must be hard for you.
☐ Time to get on with your life.
☐ Everyone's a critic.
☐ It's for the best.
☐ Don't go there.
☐ It's their loss.
☐ You can focus on your career.
☐ You can focus on your kids.
☐ Didn't kill ya; made ya stronger.
☐ Ours is not to reason why.
☐ Don't take it home with you.
☐ Timing is everything.
☐ You'll eventually love it.
☐ Think positive.
☐ Think denial.

☐ Someday you'll understand.
☐ Single life is actually better.
☐ Always darkest before the dawn.
☐ Just clear the browser history.
☐ You're still young.
☐ He isn't worth it.
☐ She isn't worth it.
☐ Where there's a will . . .
☐ Chalk it up to experience.
☐ Cross that bridge later.
☐ One day at a time.
☐ You can always get it fixed.
☐ Don't sweat the small stuff.
☐ Not over 'til the fat lady sings.
☐ It's all nonsense anyway.
☐ You gotta believe in you.
☐ I believe in you.
☐ Anything is possible.
☐ You reacted with integrity.
☐ You can sell it online.
☐ Don't get mad, get even.
☐ No one can tell it's a knockoff.
☐ Just say no.
☐ Hang in there, baby.
☐ If it's not one thing, it's another.
☐ It'll build character.
☐ It was meant to be.
☐ It wasn't meant to be.
☐ If it's meant to be, it'll happen.
☐ Keep your chin up.
☐ You don't need their approval.
☐ For every hill there's a valley.
☐ I would've done the same.
☐ Life goes on.
☐ Absence makes love stronger.
☐ Can't beat 'em? Join 'em.
☐ Shake it off.
☐ No one heard it.
☐ Better late than never.
☐ Better safe than sorry.
☐ And so it goes.
☐ The first cut is the deepest.
☐ Love hurts.
☐ Love stinks.
☐ Love is overrated.
☐ Soon this'll be a distant memory.
☐ Keep on truckin'.
☐ Quit worrying.
☐ It's water under the bridge.
☐ Don't dwell on it.

☐ Ya gotta do what ya gotta do.
☐ When it rains, it pours.
☐ Every rose has a thorn.
☐ You gave it your best shot.
☐ There, there.
☐ It takes all kinds.
☐ They're just jealous.
☐ It'll come when you're ready.
☐ Nobody mentioned it.
☐ Try to keep it in perspective.
☐ Put on your big girl panties.
☐ Put on your big boy briefs.
☐ There's a lid for every pot.
☐ He's probably out of town.
☐ Her phone is probably dead.
☐ You're better off.
☐ It happens sometimes.
☐ They don't understand you.
☐ It was an honest mistake.
☐ Money can't buy love.
☐ Adversity forges character.
☐ You'll feel better after a bath.
☐ You'll feel better after a drink.
☐ It'll make great memoir material.
☐ Quit blaming yourself.
☐ There's no such thing as normal.
☐ You'll show them.
☐ This will forge your character.
☐ You're a superstar.
☐ Just explain what happened.
☐ Don't compare.
☐ All parents screw up.
☐ All kids screw up.
☐ At least you have your health.
☐ He'll grow out of it.
☐ She'll grow out of it.
☐ Shhh. Shhh. It's okay now.
☐ Pain is temporary.
☐ I agree with you.
☐ One day you'll know why.
☐ You march to your own beat.
☐ Ignore what others think.
☐ Buck up, buckwheat.
☐ Everyone sympathizes.
☐ You're overthinking this.
☐ Get back up on the horse.
☐ Just give it some time.
☐ It's not the end of the world.
☐ It gets better.
☐ Really, it is.

☐ **TOTALLY OKAY** ☐ **PRETTY OKAY** ☐ **OKAY-ISH**

SIGNATURE

MONTH DAY YEAR

"OKAY? OKAY. OKAY!"

IT'S GONNA BE OKAY

☐ **RIGHT NOW** ☐ **FAIRLY SOON** ☐ **EVENTUALLY**

- ☐ It'll grow back.
- ☐ You'll get over it.
- ☐ You can do this.
- ☐ It wasn't that obvious.
- ☐ This too shall pass.
- ☐ You're too good for him.
- ☐ You're too good for her.
- ☐ I'll never tell.
- ☐ Don't blame yourself.
- ☐ There are other fish in the sea.
- ☐ Tattoo removal is easier now.
- ☐ You are not your job.
- ☐ Your mother will never know.
- ☐ Nothing therapy won't cure.
- ☐ Just take a mulligan.
- ☐ Moving home is no big deal.
- ☐ Don't "should" all over yourself.
- ☐ At least you know you're right.
- ☐ You did your best.
- ☐ Can't win 'em all.
- ☐ You couldn't have known.
- ☐ My cousin had that and was fine.
- ☐ Laughter is the best medicine.
- ☐ Have faith.
- ☐ Penicillin clears that up fast.
- ☐ He wasn't thinking.
- ☐ She wasn't thinking.
- ☐ If at first you don't succeed . . .
- ☐ It's about quality, not quantity.
- ☐ That's not old, it's vintage.
- ☐ You're not old, you're vintage.
- ☐ Things happen for a reason.
- ☐ It'll look better in the morning.
- ☐ You can blog about it.
- ☐ We'll look back later and laugh.
- ☐ No one will ever know.
- ☐ Here's a hug.
- ☐ They don't deserve you.
- ☐ Every cloud has a silver lining.
- ☐ It was totally his fault.
- ☐ It was totally her fault.
- ☐ A rising tide lifts all boats.
- ☐ There are specialists for that.
- ☐ Think of the big picture.
- ☐ Don't let it bother you so much.
- ☐ No one saw you trip.
- ☐ You'll get that promotion soon.
- ☐ It could've been much worse.
- ☐ Aim for the stars.
- ☐ You'll forget about it, I promise.
- ☐ All publicity is good publicity.
- ☐ You can always return it.
- ☐ That was so understandable.
- ☐ You look great.
- ☐ You look great for your age.
- ☐ That happens to everyone.
- ☐ You made your point.
- ☐ Who wants that responsibility?
- ☐ It's not more than you can handle.
- ☐ Time heals all wounds.
- ☐ Time wounds all heels.
- ☐ I'm sure you don't normally do that.
- ☐ Success or not, you are loved.
- ☐ It's a journey, not a destination.
- ☐ It was a long shot anyway.
- ☐ Lesson learned.
- ☐ It's not you, it's the economy.
- ☐ You can always sue.
- ☐ You're the bigger person.
- ☐ You still have your honor.
- ☐ You still have your hair.
- ☐ Heartbreak makes you wiser.
- ☐ People will see through that.
- ☐ You'll be the last one standing.
- ☐ Don't let it get you down.
- ☐ It's not forever.
- ☐ There are always people like that.
- ☐ Never fear, karma's a bitch.
- ☐ I think it looks cute.
- ☐ One door closes, another opens.
- ☐ It's all part of the plan.
- ☐ Go ahead, cry it out.
- ☐ They spelled your name right.
- ☐ Jobs come, jobs go.
- ☐ People come, people go.
- ☐ This must be hard for you.
- ☐ Time to get on with your life.
- ☐ Everyone's a critic.
- ☐ It's for the best.
- ☐ Don't go there.
- ☐ It's their loss.
- ☐ You can focus on your career.
- ☐ You can focus on your kids.
- ☐ Didn't kill ya; made ya stronger.
- ☐ Ours is not to reason why.
- ☐ Don't take it home with you.
- ☐ Timing is everything.
- ☐ You'll eventually love it.
- ☐ Think positive.
- ☐ Think denial.
- ☐ Someday you'll understand.
- ☐ Single life is actually better.
- ☐ Always darkest before the dawn.
- ☐ Just clear the browser history.
- ☐ You're still young.
- ☐ He isn't worth it.
- ☐ She isn't worth it.
- ☐ Where there's a will . . .
- ☐ Chalk it up to experience.
- ☐ Cross that bridge later.
- ☐ One day at a time.
- ☐ You can always get it fixed.
- ☐ Don't sweat the small stuff.
- ☐ Not over 'til the fat lady sings.
- ☐ It's all nonsense anyway.
- ☐ You gotta believe in you.
- ☐ I believe in you.
- ☐ Anything is possible.
- ☐ You reacted with integrity.
- ☐ You can sell it online.
- ☐ Don't get mad, get even.
- ☐ No one can tell it's a knockoff.
- ☐ Just say no.
- ☐ Hang in there, baby.
- ☐ If it's not one thing, it's another.
- ☐ It'll build character.
- ☐ It was meant to be.
- ☐ It wasn't meant to be.
- ☐ If it's meant to be, it'll happen.
- ☐ Keep your chin up.
- ☐ You don't need their approval.
- ☐ For every hill there's a valley.
- ☐ I would've done the same.
- ☐ Life goes on.
- ☐ Absence makes love stronger.
- ☐ Can't beat 'em? Join 'em.
- ☐ Shake it off.
- ☐ No one heard it.
- ☐ Better late than never.
- ☐ Better safe than sorry.
- ☐ And so it goes.
- ☐ The first cut is the deepest.
- ☐ Love hurts.
- ☐ Love stinks.
- ☐ Love is overrated.
- ☐ Soon this'll be a distant memory.
- ☐ Keep on truckin'.
- ☐ Quit worrying.
- ☐ It's water under the bridge.
- ☐ Don't dwell on it.
- ☐ Ya gotta do what ya gotta do.
- ☐ When it rains, it pours.
- ☐ Every rose has a thorn.
- ☐ You gave it your best shot.
- ☐ There, there.
- ☐ It takes all kinds.
- ☐ They're just jealous.
- ☐ It'll come when you're ready.
- ☐ Nobody mentioned it.
- ☐ Try to keep it in perspective.
- ☐ Put on your big girl panties.
- ☐ Put on your big boy briefs.
- ☐ There's a lid for every pot.
- ☐ He's probably out of town.
- ☐ Her phone is probably dead.
- ☐ You're better off.
- ☐ It happens sometimes.
- ☐ They don't understand you.
- ☐ It was an honest mistake.
- ☐ Money can't buy love.
- ☐ Adversity forges character.
- ☐ You'll feel better after a bath.
- ☐ You'll feel better after a drink.
- ☐ It'll make great memoir material.
- ☐ Quit blaming yourself.
- ☐ There's no such thing as normal.
- ☐ You'll show them.
- ☐ This will forge your character.
- ☐ You're a superstar.
- ☐ Just explain what happened.
- ☐ Don't compare.
- ☐ All parents screw up.
- ☐ All kids screw up.
- ☐ At least you have your health.
- ☐ He'll grow out of it.
- ☐ She'll grow out of it.
- ☐ Shhh. Shhh. It's okay now.
- ☐ Pain is temporary.
- ☐ I agree with you.
- ☐ One day you'll know why.
- ☐ You march to your own beat.
- ☐ Ignore what others think.
- ☐ Buck up, buckwheat.
- ☐ Everyone sympathizes.
- ☐ You're overthinking this.
- ☐ Get back up on the horse.
- ☐ Just give it some time.
- ☐ It's not the end of the world.
- ☐ It gets better.
- ☐ Really, it is.

☐ **TOTALLY OKAY** ☐ **PRETTY OKAY** ☐ **OKAY-ISH**

SIGNATURE MONTH DAY YEAR

"OKAY? OKAY. OKAY!"

IT'S GONNA BE OKAY

☐ **RIGHT NOW** ☐ **FAIRLY SOON** ☐ **EVENTUALLY**

☐ It'll grow back.
☐ You'll get over it.
☐ You can do this.
☐ It wasn't that obvious.
☐ This too shall pass.
☐ You're too good for him.
☐ You're too good for her.
☐ I'll never tell.
☐ Don't blame yourself.
☐ There are other fish in the sea.
☐ Tattoo removal is easier now.
☐ You are not your job.
☐ Your mother will never know.
☐ Nothing therapy won't cure.
☐ Just take a mulligan.
☐ Moving home is no big deal.
☐ Don't "should" all over yourself.
☐ At least you know you're right.
☐ You did your best.
☐ Can't win 'em all.
☐ You couldn't have known.
☐ My cousin had that and was fine.
☐ Laughter is the best medicine.
☐ Have faith.
☐ Penicillin clears that up fast.
☐ He wasn't thinking.
☐ She wasn't thinking.
☐ If at first you don't succeed . . .
☐ It's about quality, not quantity.
☐ That's not old, it's vintage.
☐ You're not old, you're vintage.
☐ Things happen for a reason.
☐ It'll look better in the morning.
☐ You can blog about it.
☐ We'll look back later and laugh.
☐ No one will ever know.
☐ Here's a hug.
☐ They don't deserve you.
☐ Every cloud has a silver lining.
☐ It was totally his fault.
☐ It was totally her fault.
☐ A rising tide lifts all boats.
☐ There are specialists for that.
☐ Think of the big picture.
☐ Don't let it bother you so much.
☐ No one saw you trip.
☐ You'll get that promotion soon.
☐ It could've been much worse.
☐ Aim for the stars.
☐ You'll forget about it, I promise.

☐ All publicity is good publicity.
☐ You can always return it.
☐ That was so understandable.
☐ You look great.
☐ You look great for your age.
☐ That happens to everyone.
☐ You made your point.
☐ Who wants that responsibility?
☐ It's not more than you can handle.
☐ Time heals all wounds.
☐ Time wounds all heels.
☐ I'm sure you don't normally do that.
☐ Success or not, you are loved.
☐ It's a journey, not a destination.
☐ It was a long shot anyway.
☐ Lesson learned.
☐ It's not you, it's the economy.
☐ You can always sue.
☐ You're the bigger person.
☐ You still have your honor.
☐ You still have your hair.
☐ Heartbreak makes you wiser.
☐ People will see through that.
☐ You'll be the last one standing.
☐ Don't let it get you down.
☐ It's not forever.
☐ There are always people like that.
☐ Never fear, karma's a bitch.
☐ I think it looks cute.
☐ One door closes, another opens.
☐ It's all part of the plan.
☐ Go ahead, cry it out.
☐ They spelled your name right.
☐ Jobs come, jobs go.
☐ People come, people go.
☐ This must be hard for you.
☐ Time to get on with your life.
☐ Everyone's a critic.
☐ It's for the best.
☐ Don't go there.
☐ It's their loss.
☐ You can focus on your career.
☐ You can focus on your kids.
☐ Didn't kill ya; made ya stronger.
☐ Ours is not to reason why.
☐ Don't take it home with you.
☐ Timing is everything.
☐ You'll eventually love it.
☐ Think positive.
☐ Think denial.

☐ Someday you'll understand.
☐ Single life is actually better.
☐ Always darkest before the dawn.
☐ Just clear the browser history.
☐ You're still young.
☐ He isn't worth it.
☐ She isn't worth it.
☐ Where there's a will . . .
☐ Chalk it up to experience.
☐ Cross that bridge later.
☐ One day at a time.
☐ You can always get it fixed.
☐ Don't sweat the small stuff.
☐ Not over 'til the fat lady sings.
☐ It's all nonsense anyway.
☐ You gotta believe in you.
☐ I believe in you.
☐ Anything is possible.
☐ You reacted with integrity.
☐ You can sell it online.
☐ Don't get mad, get even.
☐ No one can tell it's a knockoff.
☐ Just say no.
☐ Hang in there, baby.
☐ If it's not one thing, it's another.
☐ It'll build character.
☐ It was meant to be.
☐ It wasn't meant to be.
☐ If it's meant to be, it'll happen.
☐ Keep your chin up.
☐ You don't need their approval.
☐ For every hill there's a valley.
☐ I would've done the same.
☐ Life goes on.
☐ Absence makes love stronger.
☐ Can't beat 'em? Join 'em.
☐ Shake it off.
☐ No one heard it.
☐ Better late than never.
☐ Better safe than sorry.
☐ And so it goes.
☐ The first cut is the deepest.
☐ Love hurts.
☐ Love stinks.
☐ Love is overrated.
☐ Soon this'll be a distant memory.
☐ Keep on truckin'.
☐ Quit worrying.
☐ It's water under the bridge.
☐ Don't dwell on it.

☐ Ya gotta do what ya gotta do.
☐ When it rains, it pours.
☐ Every rose has a thorn.
☐ You gave it your best shot.
☐ There, there.
☐ It takes all kinds.
☐ They're just jealous.
☐ It'll come when you're ready.
☐ Nobody mentioned it.
☐ Try to keep it in perspective.
☐ Put on your big girl panties.
☐ Put on your big boy briefs.
☐ There's a lid for every pot.
☐ He's probably out of town.
☐ Her phone is probably dead.
☐ You're better off.
☐ It happens sometimes.
☐ They don't understand you.
☐ It was an honest mistake.
☐ Money can't buy love.
☐ Adversity forges character.
☐ You'll feel better after a bath.
☐ You'll feel better after a drink.
☐ It'll make great memoir material.
☐ Quit blaming yourself.
☐ There's no such thing as normal.
☐ You'll show them.
☐ This will forge your character.
☐ You're a superstar.
☐ Just explain what happened.
☐ Don't compare.
☐ All parents screw up.
☐ All kids screw up.
☐ At least you have your health.
☐ He'll grow out of it.
☐ She'll grow out of it.
☐ Shhh. Shhh. It's okay now.
☐ Pain is temporary.
☐ I agree with you.
☐ One day you'll know why.
☐ You march to your own beat.
☐ Ignore what others think.
☐ Buck up, buckwheat.
☐ Everyone sympathizes.
☐ You're overthinking this.
☐ Get back up on the horse.
☐ Just give it some time.
☐ It's not the end of the world.
☐ It gets better.
☐ Really, it is.

☐ **TOTALLY OKAY** ☐ **PRETTY OKAY** ☐ **OKAY-ISH**

SIGNATURE	MONTH	DAY	YEAR

"OKAY? OKAY. OKAY!"

IT'S GONNA BE OKAY

☐ RIGHT NOW ☐ FAIRLY SOON ☐ EVENTUALLY

- ☐ It'll grow back.
- ☐ You'll get over it.
- ☐ You can do this.
- ☐ It wasn't that obvious.
- ☐ This too shall pass.
- ☐ You're too good for him.
- ☐ You're too good for her.
- ☐ I'll never tell.
- ☐ Don't blame yourself.
- ☐ There are other fish in the sea.
- ☐ Tattoo removal is easier now.
- ☐ You are not your job.
- ☐ Your mother will never know.
- ☐ Nothing therapy won't cure.
- ☐ Just take a mulligan.
- ☐ Moving home is no big deal.
- ☐ Don't "should" all over yourself.
- ☐ At least you know you're right.
- ☐ You did your best.
- ☐ Can't win 'em all.
- ☐ You couldn't have known.
- ☐ My cousin had that and was fine.
- ☐ Laughter is the best medicine.
- ☐ Have faith.
- ☐ Penicillin clears that up fast.
- ☐ He wasn't thinking.
- ☐ She wasn't thinking.
- ☐ If at first you don't succeed . . .
- ☐ It's about quality, not quantity.
- ☐ That's not old, it's vintage.
- ☐ You're not old, you're vintage.
- ☐ Things happen for a reason.
- ☐ It'll look better in the morning.
- ☐ You can blog about it.
- ☐ We'll look back later and laugh.
- ☐ No one will ever know.
- ☐ Here's a hug.
- ☐ They don't deserve you.
- ☐ Every cloud has a silver lining.
- ☐ It was totally his fault.
- ☐ It was totally her fault.
- ☐ A rising tide lifts all boats.
- ☐ There are specialists for that.
- ☐ Think of the big picture.
- ☐ Don't let it bother you so much.
- ☐ No one saw you trip.
- ☐ You'll get that promotion soon.
- ☐ It could've been much worse.
- ☐ Aim for the stars.
- ☐ You'll forget about it, I promise.
- ☐ All publicity is good publicity.
- ☐ You can always return it.
- ☐ That was so understandable.
- ☐ You look great.
- ☐ You look great for your age.
- ☐ That happens to everyone.
- ☐ You made your point.
- ☐ Who wants that responsibility?
- ☐ It's not more than you can handle.
- ☐ Time heals all wounds.
- ☐ Time wounds all heels.
- ☐ I'm sure you don't normally do that.
- ☐ Success or not, you are loved.
- ☐ It's a journey, not a destination.
- ☐ It was a long shot anyway.
- ☐ Lesson learned.
- ☐ It's not you, it's the economy.
- ☐ You can always sue.
- ☐ You're the bigger person.
- ☐ You still have your honor.
- ☐ You still have your hair.
- ☐ Heartbreak makes you wiser.
- ☐ People will see through that.
- ☐ You'll be the last one standing.
- ☐ Don't let it get you down.
- ☐ It's not forever.
- ☐ There are always people like that.
- ☐ Never fear, karma's a bitch.
- ☐ I think it looks cute.
- ☐ One door closes, another opens.
- ☐ It's all part of the plan.
- ☐ Go ahead, cry it out.
- ☐ They spelled your name right.
- ☐ Jobs come, jobs go.
- ☐ People come, people go.
- ☐ This must be hard for you.
- ☐ Time to get on with your life.
- ☐ Everyone's a critic.
- ☐ It's for the best.
- ☐ Don't go there.
- ☐ It's their loss.
- ☐ You can focus on your career.
- ☐ You can focus on your kids.
- ☐ Didn't kill ya; made ya stronger.
- ☐ Ours is not to reason why.
- ☐ Don't take it home with you.
- ☐ Timing is everything.
- ☐ You'll eventually love it.
- ☐ Think positive.
- ☐ Think denial.
- ☐ Someday you'll understand.
- ☐ Single life is actually better.
- ☐ Always darkest before the dawn.
- ☐ Just clear the browser history.
- ☐ You're still young.
- ☐ He isn't worth it.
- ☐ She isn't worth it.
- ☐ Where there's a will . . .
- ☐ Chalk it up to experience.
- ☐ Cross that bridge later.
- ☐ One day at a time.
- ☐ You can always get it fixed.
- ☐ Don't sweat the small stuff.
- ☐ Not over 'til the fat lady sings.
- ☐ It's all nonsense anyway.
- ☐ You gotta believe in you.
- ☐ I believe in you.
- ☐ Anything is possible.
- ☐ You reacted with integrity.
- ☐ You can sell it online.
- ☐ Don't get mad, get even.
- ☐ No one can tell it's a knockoff.
- ☐ Just say no.
- ☐ Hang in there, baby.
- ☐ If it's not one thing, it's another.
- ☐ It'll build character.
- ☐ It was meant to be.
- ☐ It wasn't meant to be.
- ☐ If it's meant to be, it'll happen.
- ☐ Keep your chin up.
- ☐ You don't need their approval.
- ☐ For every hill there's a valley.
- ☐ I would've done the same.
- ☐ Life goes on.
- ☐ Absence makes love stronger.
- ☐ Can't beat 'em? Join 'em.
- ☐ Shake it off.
- ☐ No one heard it.
- ☐ Better late than never.
- ☐ Better safe than sorry.
- ☐ And so it goes.
- ☐ The first cut is the deepest.
- ☐ Love hurts.
- ☐ Love stinks.
- ☐ Love is overrated.
- ☐ Soon this'll be a distant memory.
- ☐ Keep on truckin'.
- ☐ Quit worrying.
- ☐ It's water under the bridge.
- ☐ Don't dwell on it.
- ☐ Ya gotta do what ya gotta do.
- ☐ When it rains, it pours.
- ☐ Every rose has a thorn.
- ☐ You gave it your best shot.
- ☐ There, there.
- ☐ It takes all kinds.
- ☐ They're just jealous.
- ☐ It'll come when you're ready.
- ☐ Nobody mentioned it.
- ☐ Try to keep it in perspective.
- ☐ Put on your big girl panties.
- ☐ Put on your big boy briefs.
- ☐ There's a lid for every pot.
- ☐ He's probably out of town.
- ☐ Her phone is probably dead.
- ☐ You're better off.
- ☐ It happens sometimes.
- ☐ They don't understand you.
- ☐ It was an honest mistake.
- ☐ Money can't buy love.
- ☐ Adversity forges character.
- ☐ You'll feel better after a bath.
- ☐ You'll feel better after a drink.
- ☐ It'll make great memoir material.
- ☐ Quit blaming yourself.
- ☐ There's no such thing as normal.
- ☐ You'll show them.
- ☐ This will forge your character.
- ☐ You're a superstar.
- ☐ Just explain what happened.
- ☐ Don't compare.
- ☐ All parents screw up.
- ☐ All kids screw up.
- ☐ At least you have your health.
- ☐ He'll grow out of it.
- ☐ She'll grow out of it.
- ☐ Shhh. Shhh. It's okay now.
- ☐ Pain is temporary.
- ☐ I agree with you.
- ☐ One day you'll know why.
- ☐ You march to your own beat.
- ☐ Ignore what others think.
- ☐ Buck up, buckwheat.
- ☐ Everyone sympathizes.
- ☐ You're overthinking this.
- ☐ Get back up on the horse.
- ☐ Just give it some time.
- ☐ It's not the end of the world.
- ☐ It gets better.
- ☐ Really, it is.

☐ TOTALLY OKAY ☐ PRETTY OKAY ☐ OKAY-ISH

SIGNATURE MONTH DAY YEAR

"OKAY? OKAY. OKAY!"

IT'S GONNA BE OKAY

☐ **RIGHT NOW** ☐ **FAIRLY SOON** ☐ **EVENTUALLY**

☐ It'll grow back.
☐ You'll get over it.
☐ You can do this.
☐ It wasn't that obvious.
☐ This too shall pass.
☐ You're too good for him.
☐ You're too good for her.
☐ I'll never tell.
☐ Don't blame yourself.
☐ There are other fish in the sea.
☐ Tattoo removal is easier now.
☐ You are not your job.
☐ Your mother will never know.
☐ Nothing therapy won't cure.
☐ Just take a mulligan.
☐ Moving home is no big deal.
☐ Don't "should" all over yourself.
☐ At least you know you're right.
☐ You did your best.
☐ Can't win 'em all.
☐ You couldn't have known.
☐ My cousin had that and was fine.
☐ Laughter is the best medicine.
☐ Have faith.
☐ Penicillin clears that up fast.
☐ He wasn't thinking.
☐ She wasn't thinking.
☐ If at first you don't succeed . . .
☐ It's about quality, not quantity.
☐ That's not old, it's vintage.
☐ You're not old, you're vintage.
☐ Things happen for a reason.
☐ It'll look better in the morning.
☐ You can blog about it.
☐ We'll look back later and laugh.
☐ No one will ever know.
☐ Here's a hug.
☐ They don't deserve you.
☐ Every cloud has a silver lining.
☐ It was totally his fault.
☐ It was totally her fault.
☐ A rising tide lifts all boats.
☐ There are specialists for that.
☐ Think of the big picture.
☐ Don't let it bother you so much.
☐ No one saw you trip.
☐ You'll get that promotion soon.
☐ It could've been much worse.
☐ Aim for the stars.
☐ You'll forget about it, I promise.

☐ All publicity is good publicity.
☐ You can always return it.
☐ That was so understandable.
☐ You look great.
☐ You look great for your age.
☐ That happens to everyone.
☐ You made your point.
☐ Who wants that responsibility?
☐ It's not more than you can handle.
☐ Time heals all wounds.
☐ Time wounds all heels.
☐ I'm sure you don't normally do that.
☐ Success or not, you are loved.
☐ It's a journey, not a destination.
☐ It was a long shot anyway.
☐ Lesson learned.
☐ It's not you, it's the economy.
☐ You can always sue.
☐ You're the bigger person.
☐ You still have your honor.
☐ You still have your hair.
☐ Heartbreak makes you wiser.
☐ People will see through that.
☐ You'll be the last one standing.
☐ Don't let it get you down.
☐ It's not forever.
☐ There are always people like that.
☐ Never fear, karma's a bitch.
☐ I think it looks cute.
☐ One door closes, another opens.
☐ It's all part of the plan.
☐ Go ahead, cry it out.
☐ They spelled your name right.
☐ Jobs come, jobs go.
☐ People come, people go.
☐ This must be hard for you.
☐ Time to get on with your life.
☐ Everyone's a critic.
☐ It's for the best.
☐ Don't go there.
☐ It's their loss.
☐ You can focus on your career.
☐ You can focus on your kids.
☐ Didn't kill ya; made ya stronger.
☐ Ours is not to reason why.
☐ Don't take it home with you.
☐ Timing is everything.
☐ You'll eventually love it.
☐ Think positive.
☐ Think denial.

☐ Someday you'll understand.
☐ Single life is actually better.
☐ Always darkest before the dawn.
☐ Just clear the browser history.
☐ You're still young.
☐ He isn't worth it.
☐ She isn't worth it.
☐ Where there's a will . . .
☐ Chalk it up to experience.
☐ Cross that bridge later.
☐ One day at a time.
☐ You can always get it fixed.
☐ Don't sweat the small stuff.
☐ Not over 'til the fat lady sings.
☐ It's all nonsense anyway.
☐ You gotta believe in you.
☐ I believe in you.
☐ Anything is possible.
☐ You reacted with integrity.
☐ You can sell it online.
☐ Don't get mad, get even.
☐ No one can tell it's a knockoff.
☐ Just say no.
☐ Hang in there, baby.
☐ If it's not one thing, it's another.
☐ It'll build character.
☐ It was meant to be.
☐ It wasn't meant to be.
☐ If it's meant to be, it'll happen.
☐ Keep your chin up.
☐ You don't need their approval.
☐ For every hill there's a valley.
☐ I would've done the same.
☐ Life goes on.
☐ Absence makes love stronger.
☐ Can't beat 'em? Join 'em.
☐ Shake it off.
☐ No one heard it.
☐ Better late than never.
☐ Better safe than sorry.
☐ And so it goes.
☐ The first cut is the deepest.
☐ Love hurts.
☐ Love stinks.
☐ Love is overrated.
☐ Soon this'll be a distant memory.
☐ Keep on truckin'.
☐ Quit worrying.
☐ It's water under the bridge.
☐ Don't dwell on it.

☐ Ya gotta do what ya gotta do.
☐ When it rains, it pours.
☐ Every rose has a thorn.
☐ You gave it your best shot.
☐ There, there.
☐ It takes all kinds.
☐ They're just jealous.
☐ It'll come when you're ready.
☐ Nobody mentioned it.
☐ Try to keep it in perspective.
☐ Put on your big girl panties.
☐ Put on your big boy briefs.
☐ There's a lid for every pot.
☐ He's probably out of town.
☐ Her phone is probably dead.
☐ You're better off.
☐ It happens sometimes.
☐ They don't understand you.
☐ It was an honest mistake.
☐ Money can't buy love.
☐ Adversity forges character.
☐ You'll feel better after a bath.
☐ You'll feel better after a drink.
☐ It'll make great memoir material.
☐ Quit blaming yourself.
☐ There's no such thing as normal.
☐ You'll show them.
☐ This will forge your character.
☐ You're a superstar.
☐ Just explain what happened.
☐ Don't compare.
☐ All parents screw up.
☐ All kids screw up.
☐ At least you have your health.
☐ He'll grow out of it.
☐ She'll grow out of it.
☐ Shhh. Shhh. It's okay now.
☐ Pain is temporary.
☐ I agree with you.
☐ One day you'll know why.
☐ You march to your own beat.
☐ Ignore what others think.
☐ Buck up, buckwheat.
☐ Everyone sympathizes.
☐ You're overthinking this.
☐ Get back up on the horse.
☐ Just give it some time.
☐ It's not the end of the world.
☐ It gets better.
☐ Really, it is.

☐ **TOTALLY OKAY** ☐ **PRETTY OKAY** ☐ **OKAY-ISH**

SIGNATURE

MONTH DAY YEAR

"OKAY? OKAY. OKAY!"

IT'S GONNA BE OKAY

☐ **RIGHT NOW** ☐ **FAIRLY SOON** ☐ **EVENTUALLY**

- ☐ It'll grow back.
- ☐ You'll get over it.
- ☐ You can do this.
- ☐ It wasn't that obvious.
- ☐ This too shall pass.
- ☐ You're too good for him.
- ☐ You're too good for her.
- ☐ I'll never tell.
- ☐ Don't blame yourself.
- ☐ There are other fish in the sea.
- ☐ Tattoo removal is easier now.
- ☐ You are not your job.
- ☐ Your mother will never know.
- ☐ Nothing therapy won't cure.
- ☐ Just take a mulligan.
- ☐ Moving home is no big deal.
- ☐ Don't "should" all over yourself.
- ☐ At least you know you're right.
- ☐ You did your best.
- ☐ Can't win 'em all.
- ☐ You couldn't have known.
- ☐ My cousin had that and was fine.
- ☐ Laughter is the best medicine.
- ☐ Have faith.
- ☐ Penicillin clears that up fast.
- ☐ He wasn't thinking.
- ☐ She wasn't thinking.
- ☐ If at first you don't succeed . . .
- ☐ It's about quality, not quantity.
- ☐ That's not old, it's vintage.
- ☐ You're not old, you're vintage.
- ☐ Things happen for a reason.
- ☐ It'll look better in the morning.
- ☐ You can blog about it.
- ☐ We'll look back later and laugh.
- ☐ No one will ever know.
- ☐ Here's a hug.
- ☐ They don't deserve you.
- ☐ Every cloud has a silver lining.
- ☐ It was totally his fault.
- ☐ It was totally her fault.
- ☐ A rising tide lifts all boats.
- ☐ There are specialists for that.
- ☐ Think of the big picture.
- ☐ Don't let it bother you so much.
- ☐ No one saw you trip.
- ☐ You'll get that promotion soon.
- ☐ It could've been much worse.
- ☐ Aim for the stars.
- ☐ You'll forget about it, I promise.

- ☐ All publicity is good publicity.
- ☐ You can always return it.
- ☐ That was so understandable.
- ☐ You look great.
- ☐ You look great for your age.
- ☐ That happens to everyone.
- ☐ You made your point.
- ☐ Who wants that responsibility?
- ☐ It's not more than you can handle.
- ☐ Time heals all wounds.
- ☐ Time wounds all heels.
- ☐ I'm sure you don't normally do that.
- ☐ Success or not, you are loved.
- ☐ It's a journey, not a destination.
- ☐ It was a long shot anyway.
- ☐ Lesson learned.
- ☐ It's not you, it's the economy.
- ☐ You can always sue.
- ☐ You're the bigger person.
- ☐ You still have your honor.
- ☐ You still have your hair.
- ☐ Heartbreak makes you wiser.
- ☐ People will see through that.
- ☐ You'll be the last one standing.
- ☐ Don't let it get you down.
- ☐ It's not forever.
- ☐ There are always people like that.
- ☐ Never fear, karma's a bitch.
- ☐ I think it looks cute.
- ☐ One door closes, another opens.
- ☐ It's all part of the plan.
- ☐ Go ahead, cry it out.
- ☐ They spelled your name right.
- ☐ Jobs come, jobs go.
- ☐ People come, people go.
- ☐ This must be hard for you.
- ☐ Time to get on with your life.
- ☐ Everyone's a critic.
- ☐ It's for the best.
- ☐ Don't go there.
- ☐ It's their loss.
- ☐ You can focus on your career.
- ☐ You can focus on your kids.
- ☐ Didn't kill ya; made ya stronger.
- ☐ Ours is not to reason why.
- ☐ Don't take it home with you.
- ☐ Timing is everything.
- ☐ You'll eventually love it.
- ☐ Think positive.
- ☐ Think denial.

- ☐ Someday you'll understand.
- ☐ Single life is actually better.
- ☐ Always darkest before the dawn.
- ☐ Just clear the browser history.
- ☐ You're still young.
- ☐ He isn't worth it.
- ☐ She isn't worth it.
- ☐ Where there's a will . . .
- ☐ Chalk it up to experience.
- ☐ Cross that bridge later.
- ☐ One day at a time.
- ☐ You can always get it fixed.
- ☐ Don't sweat the small stuff.
- ☐ Not over 'til the fat lady sings.
- ☐ It's all nonsense anyway.
- ☐ You gotta believe in you.
- ☐ I believe in you.
- ☐ Anything is possible.
- ☐ You reacted with integrity.
- ☐ You can sell it online.
- ☐ Don't get mad, get even.
- ☐ No one can tell it's a knockoff.
- ☐ Just say no.
- ☐ Hang in there, baby.
- ☐ If it's not one thing, it's another.
- ☐ It'll build character.
- ☐ It was meant to be.
- ☐ It wasn't meant to be.
- ☐ If it's meant to be, it'll happen.
- ☐ Keep your chin up.
- ☐ You don't need their approval.
- ☐ For every hill there's a valley.
- ☐ I would've done the same.
- ☐ Life goes on.
- ☐ Absence makes love stronger.
- ☐ Can't beat 'em? Join 'em.
- ☐ Shake it off.
- ☐ No one heard it.
- ☐ Better late than never.
- ☐ Better safe than sorry.
- ☐ And so it goes.
- ☐ The first cut is the deepest.
- ☐ Love hurts.
- ☐ Love stinks.
- ☐ Love is overrated.
- ☐ Soon this'll be a distant memory.
- ☐ Keep on truckin'.
- ☐ Quit worrying.
- ☐ It's water under the bridge.
- ☐ Don't dwell on it.

- ☐ Ya gotta do what ya gotta do.
- ☐ When it rains, it pours.
- ☐ Every rose has a thorn.
- ☐ You gave it your best shot.
- ☐ There, there.
- ☐ It takes all kinds.
- ☐ They're just jealous.
- ☐ It'll come when you're ready.
- ☐ Nobody mentioned it.
- ☐ Try to keep it in perspective.
- ☐ Put on your big girl panties.
- ☐ Put on your big boy briefs.
- ☐ There's a lid for every pot.
- ☐ He's probably out of town.
- ☐ Her phone is probably dead.
- ☐ You're better off.
- ☐ It happens sometimes.
- ☐ They don't understand you.
- ☐ It was an honest mistake.
- ☐ Money can't buy love.
- ☐ Adversity forges character.
- ☐ You'll feel better after a bath.
- ☐ You'll feel better after a drink.
- ☐ It'll make great memoir material.
- ☐ Quit blaming yourself.
- ☐ There's no such thing as normal.
- ☐ You'll show them.
- ☐ This will forge your character.
- ☐ You're a superstar.
- ☐ Just explain what happened.
- ☐ Don't compare.
- ☐ All parents screw up.
- ☐ All kids screw up.
- ☐ At least you have your health.
- ☐ He'll grow out of it.
- ☐ She'll grow out of it.
- ☐ Shhh. Shhh. It's okay now.
- ☐ Pain is temporary.
- ☐ I agree with you.
- ☐ One day you'll know why.
- ☐ You march to your own beat.
- ☐ Ignore what others think.
- ☐ Buck up, buckwheat.
- ☐ Everyone sympathizes.
- ☐ You're overthinking this.
- ☐ Get back up on the horse.
- ☐ Just give it some time.
- ☐ It's not the end of the world.
- ☐ It gets better.
- ☐ Really, it is.

☐ **TOTALLY OKAY** ☐ **PRETTY OKAY** ☐ **OKAY-ISH**

SIGNATURE MONTH DAY YEAR

"OKAY? OKAY. OKAY!"

IT'S GONNA BE OKAY

☐ **RIGHT NOW** ☐ **FAIRLY SOON** ☐ **EVENTUALLY**

- ☐ It'll grow back.
- ☐ You'll get over it.
- ☐ You can do this.
- ☐ It wasn't that obvious.
- ☐ This too shall pass.
- ☐ You're too good for him.
- ☐ You're too good for her.
- ☐ I'll never tell.
- ☐ Don't blame yourself.
- ☐ There are other fish in the sea.
- ☐ Tattoo removal is easier now.
- ☐ You are not your job.
- ☐ Your mother will never know.
- ☐ Nothing therapy won't cure.
- ☐ Just take a mulligan.
- ☐ Moving home is no big deal.
- ☐ Don't "should" all over yourself.
- ☐ At least you know you're right.
- ☐ You did your best.
- ☐ Can't win 'em all.
- ☐ You couldn't have known.
- ☐ My cousin had that and was fine.
- ☐ Laughter is the best medicine.
- ☐ Have faith.
- ☐ Penicillin clears that up fast.
- ☐ He wasn't thinking.
- ☐ She wasn't thinking.
- ☐ If at first you don't succeed . . .
- ☐ It's about quality, not quantity.
- ☐ That's not old, it's vintage.
- ☐ You're not old, you're vintage.
- ☐ Things happen for a reason.
- ☐ It'll look better in the morning.
- ☐ You can blog about it.
- ☐ We'll look back later and laugh.
- ☐ No one will ever know.
- ☐ Here's a hug.
- ☐ They don't deserve you.
- ☐ Every cloud has a silver lining.
- ☐ It was totally his fault.
- ☐ It was totally her fault.
- ☐ A rising tide lifts all boats.
- ☐ There are specialists for that.
- ☐ Think of the big picture.
- ☐ Don't let it bother you so much.
- ☐ No one saw you trip.
- ☐ You'll get that promotion soon.
- ☐ It could've been much worse.
- ☐ Aim for the stars.
- ☐ You'll forget about it, I promise.
- ☐ All publicity is good publicity.
- ☐ You can always return it.
- ☐ That was so understandable.
- ☐ You look great.
- ☐ You look great for your age.
- ☐ That happens to everyone.
- ☐ You made your point.
- ☐ Who wants that responsibility?
- ☐ It's not more than you can handle.
- ☐ Time heals all wounds.
- ☐ Time wounds all heels.
- ☐ I'm sure you don't normally do that.
- ☐ Success or not, you are loved.
- ☐ It's a journey, not a destination.
- ☐ It was a long shot anyway.
- ☐ Lesson learned.
- ☐ It's not you, it's the economy.
- ☐ You can always sue.
- ☐ You're the bigger person.
- ☐ You still have your honor.
- ☐ You still have your hair.
- ☐ Heartbreak makes you wiser.
- ☐ People will see through that.
- ☐ You'll be the last one standing.
- ☐ Don't let it get you down.
- ☐ It's not forever.
- ☐ There are always people like that.
- ☐ Never fear, karma's a bitch.
- ☐ I think it looks cute.
- ☐ One door closes, another opens.
- ☐ It's all part of the plan.
- ☐ Go ahead, cry it out.
- ☐ They spelled your name right.
- ☐ Jobs come, jobs go.
- ☐ People come, people go.
- ☐ This must be hard for you.
- ☐ Time to get on with your life.
- ☐ Everyone's a critic.
- ☐ It's for the best.
- ☐ Don't go there.
- ☐ It's their loss.
- ☐ You can focus on your career.
- ☐ You can focus on your kids.
- ☐ Didn't kill ya; made ya stronger.
- ☐ Ours is not to reason why.
- ☐ Don't take it home with you.
- ☐ Timing is everything.
- ☐ You'll eventually love it.
- ☐ Think positive.
- ☐ Think denial.
- ☐ Someday you'll understand.
- ☐ Single life is actually better.
- ☐ Always darkest before the dawn.
- ☐ Just clear the browser history.
- ☐ You're still young.
- ☐ He isn't worth it.
- ☐ She isn't worth it.
- ☐ Where there's a will . . .
- ☐ Chalk it up to experience.
- ☐ Cross that bridge later.
- ☐ One day at a time.
- ☐ You can always get it fixed.
- ☐ Don't sweat the small stuff.
- ☐ Not over 'til the fat lady sings.
- ☐ It's all nonsense anyway.
- ☐ You gotta believe in you.
- ☐ I believe in you.
- ☐ Anything is possible.
- ☐ You reacted with integrity.
- ☐ You can sell it online.
- ☐ Don't get mad, get even.
- ☐ No one can tell it's a knockoff.
- ☐ Just say no.
- ☐ Hang in there, baby.
- ☐ If it's not one thing, it's another.
- ☐ It'll build character.
- ☐ It was meant to be.
- ☐ It wasn't meant to be.
- ☐ If it's meant to be, it'll happen.
- ☐ Keep your chin up.
- ☐ You don't need their approval.
- ☐ For every hill there's a valley.
- ☐ I would've done the same.
- ☐ Life goes on.
- ☐ Absence makes love stronger.
- ☐ Can't beat 'em? Join 'em.
- ☐ Shake it off.
- ☐ No one heard it.
- ☐ Better late than never.
- ☐ Better safe than sorry.
- ☐ And so it goes.
- ☐ The first cut is the deepest.
- ☐ Love hurts.
- ☐ Love stinks.
- ☐ Love is overrated.
- ☐ Soon this'll be a distant memory.
- ☐ Keep on truckin'.
- ☐ Quit worrying.
- ☐ It's water under the bridge.
- ☐ Don't dwell on it.
- ☐ Ya gotta do what ya gotta do.
- ☐ When it rains, it pours.
- ☐ Every rose has a thorn.
- ☐ You gave it your best shot.
- ☐ There, there.
- ☐ It takes all kinds.
- ☐ They're just jealous.
- ☐ It'll come when you're ready.
- ☐ Nobody mentioned it.
- ☐ Try to keep it in perspective.
- ☐ Put on your big girl panties.
- ☐ Put on your big boy briefs.
- ☐ There's a lid for every pot.
- ☐ He's probably out of town.
- ☐ Her phone is probably dead.
- ☐ You're better off.
- ☐ It happens sometimes.
- ☐ They don't understand you.
- ☐ It was an honest mistake.
- ☐ Money can't buy love.
- ☐ Adversity forges character.
- ☐ You'll feel better after a bath.
- ☐ You'll feel better after a drink.
- ☐ It'll make great memoir material.
- ☐ Quit blaming yourself.
- ☐ There's no such thing as normal.
- ☐ You'll show them.
- ☐ This will forge your character.
- ☐ You're a superstar.
- ☐ Just explain what happened.
- ☐ Don't compare.
- ☐ All parents screw up.
- ☐ All kids screw up.
- ☐ At least you have your health.
- ☐ He'll grow out of it.
- ☐ She'll grow out of it.
- ☐ Shhh. Shhh. It's okay now.
- ☐ Pain is temporary.
- ☐ I agree with you.
- ☐ One day you'll know why.
- ☐ You march to your own beat.
- ☐ Ignore what others think.
- ☐ Buck up, buckwheat.
- ☐ Everyone sympathizes.
- ☐ You're overthinking this.
- ☐ Get back up on the horse.
- ☐ Just give it some time.
- ☐ It's not the end of the world.
- ☐ It gets better.
- ☐ Really, it is.

☐ **TOTALLY OKAY** ☐ **PRETTY OKAY** ☐ **OKAY-ISH**

SIGNATURE

MONTH DAY YEAR

"OKAY? OKAY. OKAY!"

IT'S GONNA BE OKAY

☐ **RIGHT NOW** ☐ **FAIRLY SOON** ☐ **EVENTUALLY**

☐ It'll grow back.
☐ You'll get over it.
☐ You can do this.
☐ It wasn't that obvious.
☐ This too shall pass.
☐ You're too good for him.
☐ You're too good for her.
☐ I'll never tell.
☐ Don't blame yourself.
☐ There are other fish in the sea.
☐ Tattoo removal is easier now.
☐ You are not your job.
☐ Your mother will never know.
☐ Nothing therapy won't cure.
☐ Just take a mulligan.
☐ Moving home is no big deal.
☐ Don't "should" all over yourself.
☐ At least you know you're right.
☐ You did your best.
☐ Can't win 'em all.
☐ You couldn't have known.
☐ My cousin had that and was fine.
☐ Laughter is the best medicine.
☐ Have faith.
☐ Penicillin clears that up fast.
☐ He wasn't thinking.
☐ She wasn't thinking.
☐ If at first you don't succeed . . .
☐ It's about quality, not quantity.
☐ That's not old, it's vintage.
☐ You're not old, you're vintage.
☐ Things happen for a reason.
☐ It'll look better in the morning.
☐ You can blog about it.
☐ We'll look back later and laugh.
☐ No one will ever know.
☐ Here's a hug.
☐ They don't deserve you.
☐ Every cloud has a silver lining.
☐ It was totally his fault.
☐ It was totally her fault.
☐ A rising tide lifts all boats.
☐ There are specialists for that.
☐ Think of the big picture.
☐ Don't let it bother you so much.
☐ No one saw you trip.
☐ You'll get that promotion soon.
☐ It could've been much worse.
☐ Aim for the stars.
☐ You'll forget about it, I promise.

☐ All publicity is good publicity.
☐ You can always return it.
☐ That was so understandable.
☐ You look great.
☐ You look great for your age.
☐ That happens to everyone.
☐ You made your point.
☐ Who wants that responsibility?
☐ It's not more than you can handle.
☐ Time heals all wounds.
☐ Time wounds all heels.
☐ I'm sure you don't normally do that.
☐ Success or not, you are loved.
☐ It's a journey, not a destination.
☐ It was a long shot anyway.
☐ Lesson learned.
☐ It's not you, it's the economy.
☐ You can always sue.
☐ You're the bigger person.
☐ You still have your honor.
☐ You still have your hair.
☐ Heartbreak makes you wiser.
☐ People will see through that.
☐ You'll be the last one standing.
☐ Don't let it get you down.
☐ It's not forever.
☐ There are always people like that.
☐ Never fear, karma's a bitch.
☐ I think it looks cute.
☐ One door closes, another opens.
☐ It's all part of the plan.
☐ Go ahead, cry it out.
☐ They spelled your name right.
☐ Jobs come, jobs go.
☐ People come, people go.
☐ This must be hard for you.
☐ Time to get on with your life.
☐ Everyone's a critic.
☐ It's for the best.
☐ Don't go there.
☐ It's their loss.
☐ You can focus on your career.
☐ You can focus on your kids.
☐ Didn't kill ya; made ya stronger.
☐ Ours is not to reason why.
☐ Don't take it home with you.
☐ Timing is everything.
☐ You'll eventually love it.
☐ Think positive.
☐ Think denial.

☐ Someday you'll understand.
☐ Single life is actually better.
☐ Always darkest before the dawn.
☐ Just clear the browser history.
☐ You're still young.
☐ He isn't worth it.
☐ She isn't worth it.
☐ Where there's a will . . .
☐ Chalk it up to experience.
☐ Cross that bridge later.
☐ One day at a time.
☐ You can always get it fixed.
☐ Don't sweat the small stuff.
☐ Not over 'til the fat lady sings.
☐ It's all nonsense anyway.
☐ You gotta believe in you.
☐ I believe in you.
☐ Anything is possible.
☐ You reacted with integrity.
☐ You can sell it online.
☐ Don't get mad, get even.
☐ No one can tell it's a knockoff.
☐ Just say no.
☐ Hang in there, baby.
☐ If it's not one thing, it's another.
☐ It'll build character.
☐ It was meant to be.
☐ It wasn't meant to be.
☐ If it's meant to be, it'll happen.
☐ Keep your chin up.
☐ You don't need their approval.
☐ For every hill there's a valley.
☐ I would've done the same.
☐ Life goes on.
☐ Absence makes love stronger.
☐ Can't beat 'em? Join 'em.
☐ Shake it off.
☐ No one heard it.
☐ Better late than never.
☐ Better safe than sorry.
☐ And so it goes.
☐ The first cut is the deepest.
☐ Love hurts.
☐ Love stinks.
☐ Love is overrated.
☐ Soon this'll be a distant memory.
☐ Keep on truckin'.
☐ Quit worrying.
☐ It's water under the bridge.
☐ Don't dwell on it.

☐ Ya gotta do what ya gotta do.
☐ When it rains, it pours.
☐ Every rose has a thorn.
☐ You gave it your best shot.
☐ There, there.
☐ It takes all kinds.
☐ They're just jealous.
☐ It'll come when you're ready.
☐ Nobody mentioned it.
☐ Try to keep it in perspective.
☐ Put on your big girl panties.
☐ Put on your big boy briefs.
☐ There's a lid for every pot.
☐ He's probably out of town.
☐ Her phone is probably dead.
☐ You're better off.
☐ It happens sometimes.
☐ They don't understand you.
☐ It was an honest mistake.
☐ Money can't buy love.
☐ Adversity forges character.
☐ You'll feel better after a bath.
☐ You'll feel better after a drink.
☐ It'll make great memoir material.
☐ Quit blaming yourself.
☐ There's no such thing as normal.
☐ You'll show them.
☐ This will forge your character.
☐ You're a superstar.
☐ Just explain what happened.
☐ Don't compare.
☐ All parents screw up.
☐ All kids screw up.
☐ At least you have your health.
☐ He'll grow out of it.
☐ She'll grow out of it.
☐ Shhh. Shhh. It's okay now.
☐ Pain is temporary.
☐ I agree with you.
☐ One day you'll know why.
☐ You march to your own beat.
☐ Ignore what others think.
☐ Buck up, buckwheat.
☐ Everyone sympathizes.
☐ You're overthinking this.
☐ Get back up on the horse.
☐ Just give it some time.
☐ It's not the end of the world.
☐ It gets better.
☐ Really, it is.

☐ **TOTALLY OKAY** ☐ **PRETTY OKAY** ☐ **OKAY-ISH**

SIGNATURE MONTH DAY YEAR

"OKAY? OKAY. OKAY!"

IT'S GONNA BE OKAY

☐ **RIGHT NOW** ☐ **FAIRLY SOON** ☐ **EVENTUALLY**

☐ It'll grow back.
☐ You'll get over it.
☐ You can do this.
☐ It wasn't that obvious.
☐ This too shall pass.
☐ You're too good for him.
☐ You're too good for her.
☐ I'll never tell.
☐ Don't blame yourself.
☐ There are other fish in the sea.
☐ Tattoo removal is easier now.
☐ You are not your job.
☐ Your mother will never know.
☐ Nothing therapy won't cure.
☐ Just take a mulligan.
☐ Moving home is no big deal.
☐ Don't "should" all over yourself.
☐ At least you know you're right.
☐ You did your best.
☐ Can't win 'em all.
☐ You couldn't have known.
☐ My cousin had that and was fine.
☐ Laughter is the best medicine.
☐ Have faith.
☐ Penicillin clears that up fast.
☐ He wasn't thinking.
☐ She wasn't thinking.
☐ If at first you don't succeed . . .
☐ It's about quality, not quantity.
☐ That's not old, it's vintage.
☐ You're not old, you're vintage.
☐ Things happen for a reason.
☐ It'll look better in the morning.
☐ You can blog about it.
☐ We'll look back later and laugh.
☐ No one will ever know.
☐ Here's a hug.
☐ They don't deserve you.
☐ Every cloud has a silver lining.
☐ It was totally his fault.
☐ It was totally her fault.
☐ A rising tide lifts all boats.
☐ There are specialists for that.
☐ Think of the big picture.
☐ Don't let it bother you so much.
☐ No one saw you trip.
☐ You'll get that promotion soon.
☐ It could've been much worse.
☐ Aim for the stars.
☐ You'll forget about it, I promise.

☐ All publicity is good publicity.
☐ You can always return it.
☐ That was so understandable.
☐ You look great.
☐ You look great for your age.
☐ That happens to everyone.
☐ You made your point.
☐ Who wants that responsibility?
☐ It's not more than you can handle.
☐ Time heals all wounds.
☐ Time wounds all heels.
☐ I'm sure you don't normally do that.
☐ Success or not, you are loved.
☐ It's a journey, not a destination.
☐ It was a long shot anyway.
☐ Lesson learned.
☐ It's not you, it's the economy.
☐ You can always sue.
☐ You're the bigger person.
☐ You still have your honor.
☐ You still have your hair.
☐ Heartbreak makes you wiser.
☐ People will see through that.
☐ You'll be the last one standing.
☐ Don't let it get you down.
☐ It's not forever.
☐ There are always people like that.
☐ Never fear, karma's a bitch.
☐ I think it looks cute.
☐ One door closes, another opens.
☐ It's all part of the plan.
☐ Go ahead, cry it out.
☐ They spelled your name right.
☐ Jobs come, jobs go.
☐ People come, people go.
☐ This must be hard for you.
☐ Time to get on with your life.
☐ Everyone's a critic.
☐ It's for the best.
☐ Don't go there.
☐ It's their loss.
☐ You can focus on your career.
☐ You can focus on your kids.
☐ Didn't kill ya; made ya stronger.
☐ Ours is not to reason why.
☐ Don't take it home with you.
☐ Timing is everything.
☐ You'll eventually love it.
☐ Think positive.
☐ Think denial.

☐ Someday you'll understand.
☐ Single life is actually better.
☐ Always darkest before the dawn.
☐ Just clear the browser history.
☐ You're still young.
☐ He isn't worth it.
☐ She isn't worth it.
☐ Where there's a will . . .
☐ Chalk it up to experience.
☐ Cross that bridge later.
☐ One day at a time.
☐ You can always get it fixed.
☐ Don't sweat the small stuff.
☐ Not over 'til the fat lady sings.
☐ It's all nonsense anyway.
☐ You gotta believe in you.
☐ I believe in you.
☐ Anything is possible.
☐ You reacted with integrity.
☐ You can sell it online.
☐ Don't get mad, get even.
☐ No one can tell it's a knockoff.
☐ Just say no.
☐ Hang in there, baby.
☐ If it's not one thing, it's another.
☐ It'll build character.
☐ It was meant to be.
☐ It wasn't meant to be.
☐ If it's meant to be, it'll happen.
☐ Keep your chin up.
☐ You don't need their approval.
☐ For every hill there's a valley.
☐ I would've done the same.
☐ Life goes on.
☐ Absence makes love stronger.
☐ Can't beat 'em? Join 'em.
☐ Shake it off.
☐ No one heard it.
☐ Better late than never.
☐ Better safe than sorry.
☐ And so it goes.
☐ The first cut is the deepest.
☐ Love hurts.
☐ Love stinks.
☐ Love is overrated.
☐ Soon this'll be a distant memory.
☐ Keep on truckin'.
☐ Quit worrying.
☐ It's water under the bridge.
☐ Don't dwell on it.

☐ Ya gotta do what ya gotta do.
☐ When it rains, it pours.
☐ Every rose has a thorn.
☐ You gave it your best shot.
☐ There, there.
☐ It takes all kinds.
☐ They're just jealous.
☐ It'll come when you're ready.
☐ Nobody mentioned it.
☐ Try to keep it in perspective.
☐ Put on your big girl panties.
☐ Put on your big boy briefs.
☐ There's a lid for every pot.
☐ He's probably out of town.
☐ Her phone is probably dead.
☐ You're better off.
☐ It happens sometimes.
☐ They don't understand you.
☐ It was an honest mistake.
☐ Money can't buy love.
☐ Adversity forges character.
☐ You'll feel better after a bath.
☐ You'll feel better after a drink.
☐ It'll make great memoir material.
☐ Quit blaming yourself.
☐ There's no such thing as normal.
☐ You'll show them.
☐ This will forge your character.
☐ You're a superstar.
☐ Just explain what happened.
☐ Don't compare.
☐ All parents screw up.
☐ All kids screw up.
☐ At least you have your health.
☐ He'll grow out of it.
☐ She'll grow out of it.
☐ Shhh. Shhh. It's okay now.
☐ Pain is temporary.
☐ I agree with you.
☐ One day you'll know why.
☐ You march to your own beat.
☐ Ignore what others think.
☐ Buck up, buckwheat.
☐ Everyone sympathizes.
☐ You're overthinking this.
☐ Get back up on the horse.
☐ Just give it some time.
☐ It's not the end of the world.
☐ It gets better.
☐ Really, it is.

☐ **TOTALLY OKAY** ☐ **PRETTY OKAY** ☐ **OKAY-ISH**

SIGNATURE MONTH DAY YEAR

"OKAY? OKAY. OKAY!"

IT'S GONNA BE OKAY

☐ **RIGHT NOW** ☐ **FAIRLY SOON** ☐ **EVENTUALLY**

☐ It'll grow back.
☐ You'll get over it.
☐ You can do this.
☐ It wasn't that obvious.
☐ This too shall pass.
☐ You're too good for him.
☐ You're too good for her.
☐ I'll never tell.
☐ Don't blame yourself.
☐ There are other fish in the sea.
☐ Tattoo removal is easier now.
☐ You are not your job.
☐ Your mother will never know.
☐ Nothing therapy won't cure.
☐ Just take a mulligan.
☐ Moving home is no big deal.
☐ Don't "should" all over yourself.
☐ At least you know you're right.
☐ You did your best.
☐ Can't win 'em all.
☐ You couldn't have known.
☐ My cousin had that and was fine.
☐ Laughter is the best medicine.
☐ Have faith.
☐ Penicillin clears that up fast.
☐ He wasn't thinking.
☐ She wasn't thinking.
☐ If at first you don't succeed . . .
☐ It's about quality, not quantity.
☐ That's not old, it's vintage.
☐ You're not old, you're vintage.
☐ Things happen for a reason.
☐ It'll look better in the morning.
☐ You can blog about it.
☐ We'll look back later and laugh.
☐ No one will ever know.
☐ Here's a hug.
☐ They don't deserve you.
☐ Every cloud has a silver lining.
☐ It was totally his fault.
☐ It was totally her fault.
☐ A rising tide lifts all boats.
☐ There are specialists for that.
☐ Think of the big picture.
☐ Don't let it bother you so much.
☐ No one saw you trip.
☐ You'll get that promotion soon.
☐ It could've been much worse.
☐ Aim for the stars.
☐ You'll forget about it, I promise.

☐ All publicity is good publicity.
☐ You can always return it.
☐ That was so understandable.
☐ You look great.
☐ You look great for your age.
☐ That happens to everyone.
☐ You made your point.
☐ Who wants that responsibility?
☐ It's not more than you can handle.
☐ Time heals all wounds.
☐ Time wounds all heels.
☐ I'm sure you don't normally do that.
☐ Success or not, you are loved.
☐ It's a journey, not a destination.
☐ It was a long shot anyway.
☐ Lesson learned.
☐ It's not you, it's the economy.
☐ You can always sue.
☐ You're the bigger person.
☐ You still have your honor.
☐ You still have your hair.
☐ Heartbreak makes you wiser.
☐ People will see through that.
☐ You'll be the last one standing.
☐ Don't let it get you down.
☐ It's not forever.
☐ There are always people like that.
☐ Never fear, karma's a bitch.
☐ I think it looks cute.
☐ One door closes, another opens.
☐ It's all part of the plan.
☐ Go ahead, cry it out.
☐ They spelled your name right.
☐ Jobs come, jobs go.
☐ People come, people go.
☐ This must be hard for you.
☐ Time to get on with your life.
☐ Everyone's a critic.
☐ It's for the best.
☐ Don't go there.
☐ It's their loss.
☐ You can focus on your career.
☐ You can focus on your kids.
☐ Didn't kill ya; made ya stronger.
☐ Ours is not to reason why.
☐ Don't take it home with you.
☐ Timing is everything.
☐ You'll eventually love it.
☐ Think positive.
☐ Think denial.

☐ Someday you'll understand.
☐ Single life is actually better.
☐ Always darkest before the dawn.
☐ Just clear the browser history.
☐ You're still young.
☐ He isn't worth it.
☐ She isn't worth it.
☐ Where there's a will . . .
☐ Chalk it up to experience.
☐ Cross that bridge later.
☐ One day at a time.
☐ You can always get it fixed.
☐ Don't sweat the small stuff.
☐ Not over 'til the fat lady sings.
☐ It's all nonsense anyway.
☐ You gotta believe in you.
☐ I believe in you.
☐ Anything is possible.
☐ You reacted with integrity.
☐ You can sell it online.
☐ Don't get mad, get even.
☐ No one can tell it's a knockoff.
☐ Just say no.
☐ Hang in there, baby.
☐ If it's not one thing, it's another.
☐ It'll build character.
☐ It was meant to be.
☐ It wasn't meant to be.
☐ If it's meant to be, it'll happen.
☐ Keep your chin up.
☐ You don't need their approval.
☐ For every hill there's a valley.
☐ I would've done the same.
☐ Life goes on.
☐ Absence makes love stronger.
☐ Can't beat 'em? Join 'em.
☐ Shake it off.
☐ No one heard it.
☐ Better late than never.
☐ Better safe than sorry.
☐ And so it goes.
☐ The first cut is the deepest.
☐ Love hurts.
☐ Love stinks.
☐ Love is overrated.
☐ Soon this'll be a distant memory.
☐ Keep on truckin'.
☐ Quit worrying.
☐ It's water under the bridge.
☐ Don't dwell on it.

☐ Ya gotta do what ya gotta do.
☐ When it rains, it pours.
☐ Every rose has a thorn.
☐ You gave it your best shot.
☐ There, there.
☐ It takes all kinds.
☐ They're just jealous.
☐ It'll come when you're ready.
☐ Nobody mentioned it.
☐ Try to keep it in perspective.
☐ Put on your big girl panties.
☐ Put on your big boy briefs.
☐ There's a lid for every pot.
☐ He's probably out of town.
☐ Her phone is probably dead.
☐ You're better off.
☐ It happens sometimes.
☐ They don't understand you.
☐ It was an honest mistake.
☐ Money can't buy love.
☐ Adversity forges character.
☐ You'll feel better after a bath.
☐ You'll feel better after a drink.
☐ It'll make great memoir material.
☐ Quit blaming yourself.
☐ There's no such thing as normal.
☐ You'll show them.
☐ This will forge your character.
☐ You're a superstar.
☐ Just explain what happened.
☐ Don't compare.
☐ All parents screw up.
☐ All kids screw up.
☐ At least you have your health.
☐ He'll grow out of it.
☐ She'll grow out of it.
☐ Shhh. Shhh. It's okay now.
☐ Pain is temporary.
☐ I agree with you.
☐ One day you'll know why.
☐ You march to your own beat.
☐ Ignore what others think.
☐ Buck up, buckwheat.
☐ Everyone sympathizes.
☐ You're overthinking this.
☐ Get back up on the horse.
☐ Just give it some time.
☐ It's not the end of the world.
☐ It gets better.
☐ Really, it is.

☐ **TOTALLY OKAY** ☐ **PRETTY OKAY** ☐ **OKAY-ISH**

SIGNATURE MONTH DAY YEAR

"OKAY? OKAY. OKAY!"

IT'S GONNA BE OKAY

☐ **RIGHT NOW** ☐ **FAIRLY SOON** ☐ **EVENTUALLY**

- ☐ It'll grow back.
- ☐ You'll get over it.
- ☐ You can do this.
- ☐ It wasn't that obvious.
- ☐ This too shall pass.
- ☐ You're too good for him.
- ☐ You're too good for her.
- ☐ I'll never tell.
- ☐ Don't blame yourself.
- ☐ There are other fish in the sea.
- ☐ Tattoo removal is easier now.
- ☐ You are not your job.
- ☐ Your mother will never know.
- ☐ Nothing therapy won't cure.
- ☐ Just take a mulligan.
- ☐ Moving home is no big deal.
- ☐ Don't "should" all over yourself.
- ☐ At least you know you're right.
- ☐ You did your best.
- ☐ Can't win 'em all.
- ☐ You couldn't have known.
- ☐ My cousin had that and was fine.
- ☐ Laughter is the best medicine.
- ☐ Have faith.
- ☐ Penicillin clears that up fast.
- ☐ He wasn't thinking.
- ☐ She wasn't thinking.
- ☐ If at first you don't succeed . . .
- ☐ It's about quality, not quantity.
- ☐ That's not old, it's vintage.
- ☐ You're not old, you're vintage.
- ☐ Things happen for a reason.
- ☐ It'll look better in the morning.
- ☐ You can blog about it.
- ☐ We'll look back later and laugh.
- ☐ No one will ever know.
- ☐ Here's a hug.
- ☐ They don't deserve you.
- ☐ Every cloud has a silver lining.
- ☐ It was totally his fault.
- ☐ It was totally her fault.
- ☐ A rising tide lifts all boats.
- ☐ There are specialists for that.
- ☐ Think of the big picture.
- ☐ Don't let it bother you so much.
- ☐ No one saw you trip.
- ☐ You'll get that promotion soon.
- ☐ It could've been much worse.
- ☐ Aim for the stars.
- ☐ You'll forget about it, I promise.
- ☐ All publicity is good publicity.
- ☐ You can always return it.
- ☐ That was so understandable.
- ☐ You look great.
- ☐ You look great for your age.
- ☐ That happens to everyone.
- ☐ You made your point.
- ☐ Who wants that responsibility?
- ☐ It's not more than you can handle.
- ☐ Time heals all wounds.
- ☐ Time wounds all heels.
- ☐ I'm sure you don't normally do that.
- ☐ Success or not, you are loved.
- ☐ It's a journey, not a destination.
- ☐ It was a long shot anyway.
- ☐ Lesson learned.
- ☐ It's not you, it's the economy.
- ☐ You can always sue.
- ☐ You're the bigger person.
- ☐ You still have your honor.
- ☐ You still have your hair.
- ☐ Heartbreak makes you wiser.
- ☐ People will see through that.
- ☐ You'll be the last one standing.
- ☐ Don't let it get you down.
- ☐ It's not forever.
- ☐ There are always people like that.
- ☐ Never fear, karma's a bitch.
- ☐ I think it looks cute.
- ☐ One door closes, another opens.
- ☐ It's all part of the plan.
- ☐ Go ahead, cry it out.
- ☐ They spelled your name right.
- ☐ Jobs come, jobs go.
- ☐ People come, people go.
- ☐ This must be hard for you.
- ☐ Time to get on with your life.
- ☐ Everyone's a critic.
- ☐ It's for the best.
- ☐ Don't go there.
- ☐ It's their loss.
- ☐ You can focus on your career.
- ☐ You can focus on your kids.
- ☐ Didn't kill ya; made ya stronger.
- ☐ Ours is not to reason why.
- ☐ Don't take it home with you.
- ☐ Timing is everything.
- ☐ You'll eventually love it.
- ☐ Think positive.
- ☐ Think denial.
- ☐ Someday you'll understand.
- ☐ Single life is actually better.
- ☐ Always darkest before the dawn.
- ☐ Just clear the browser history.
- ☐ You're still young.
- ☐ He isn't worth it.
- ☐ She isn't worth it.
- ☐ Where there's a will . . .
- ☐ Chalk it up to experience.
- ☐ Cross that bridge later.
- ☐ One day at a time.
- ☐ You can always get it fixed.
- ☐ Don't sweat the small stuff.
- ☐ Not over 'til the fat lady sings.
- ☐ It's all nonsense anyway.
- ☐ You gotta believe in you.
- ☐ I believe in you.
- ☐ Anything is possible.
- ☐ You reacted with integrity.
- ☐ You can sell it online.
- ☐ Don't get mad, get even.
- ☐ No one can tell it's a knockoff.
- ☐ Just say no.
- ☐ Hang in there, baby.
- ☐ If it's not one thing, it's another.
- ☐ It'll build character.
- ☐ It was meant to be.
- ☐ It wasn't meant to be.
- ☐ If it's meant to be, it'll happen.
- ☐ Keep your chin up.
- ☐ You don't need their approval.
- ☐ For every hill there's a valley.
- ☐ I would've done the same.
- ☐ Life goes on.
- ☐ Absence makes love stronger.
- ☐ Can't beat 'em? Join 'em.
- ☐ Shake it off.
- ☐ No one heard it.
- ☐ Better late than never.
- ☐ Better safe than sorry.
- ☐ And so it goes.
- ☐ The first cut is the deepest.
- ☐ Love hurts.
- ☐ Love stinks.
- ☐ Love is overrated.
- ☐ Soon this'll be a distant memory.
- ☐ Keep on truckin'.
- ☐ Quit worrying.
- ☐ It's water under the bridge.
- ☐ Don't dwell on it.
- ☐ Ya gotta do what ya gotta do.
- ☐ When it rains, it pours.
- ☐ Every rose has a thorn.
- ☐ You gave it your best shot.
- ☐ There, there.
- ☐ It takes all kinds.
- ☐ They're just jealous.
- ☐ It'll come when you're ready.
- ☐ Nobody mentioned it.
- ☐ Try to keep it in perspective.
- ☐ Put on your big girl panties.
- ☐ Put on your big boy briefs.
- ☐ There's a lid for every pot.
- ☐ He's probably out of town.
- ☐ Her phone is probably dead.
- ☐ You're better off.
- ☐ It happens sometimes.
- ☐ They don't understand you.
- ☐ It was an honest mistake.
- ☐ Money can't buy love.
- ☐ Adversity forges character.
- ☐ You'll feel better after a bath.
- ☐ You'll feel better after a drink.
- ☐ It'll make great memoir material.
- ☐ Quit blaming yourself.
- ☐ There's no such thing as normal.
- ☐ You'll show them.
- ☐ This will forge your character.
- ☐ You're a superstar.
- ☐ Just explain what happened.
- ☐ Don't compare.
- ☐ All parents screw up.
- ☐ All kids screw up.
- ☐ At least you have your health.
- ☐ He'll grow out of it.
- ☐ She'll grow out of it.
- ☐ Shhh. Shhh. It's okay now.
- ☐ Pain is temporary.
- ☐ I agree with you.
- ☐ One day you'll know why.
- ☐ You march to your own beat.
- ☐ Ignore what others think.
- ☐ Buck up, buckwheat.
- ☐ Everyone sympathizes.
- ☐ You're overthinking this.
- ☐ Get back up on the horse.
- ☐ Just give it some time.
- ☐ It's not the end of the world.
- ☐ It gets better.
- ☐ Really, it is.

☐ **TOTALLY OKAY** ☐ **PRETTY OKAY** ☐ **OKAY-ISH**

SIGNATURE

MONTH DAY YEAR

"OKAY? OKAY. OKAY!"

IT'S GONNA BE OKAY

☐ **RIGHT NOW** ☐ **FAIRLY SOON** ☐ **EVENTUALLY**

- ☐ It'll grow back.
- ☐ You'll get over it.
- ☐ You can do this.
- ☐ It wasn't that obvious.
- ☐ This too shall pass.
- ☐ You're too good for him.
- ☐ You're too good for her.
- ☐ I'll never tell.
- ☐ Don't blame yourself.
- ☐ There are other fish in the sea.
- ☐ Tattoo removal is easier now.
- ☐ You are not your job.
- ☐ Your mother will never know.
- ☐ Nothing therapy won't cure.
- ☐ Just take a mulligan.
- ☐ Moving home is no big deal.
- ☐ Don't "should" all over yourself.
- ☐ At least you know you're right.
- ☐ You did your best.
- ☐ Can't win 'em all.
- ☐ You couldn't have known.
- ☐ My cousin had that and was fine.
- ☐ Laughter is the best medicine.
- ☐ Have faith.
- ☐ Penicillin clears that up fast.
- ☐ He wasn't thinking.
- ☐ She wasn't thinking.
- ☐ If at first you don't succeed . . .
- ☐ It's about quality, not quantity.
- ☐ That's not old, it's vintage.
- ☐ You're not old, you're vintage.
- ☐ Things happen for a reason.
- ☐ It'll look better in the morning.
- ☐ You can blog about it.
- ☐ We'll look back later and laugh.
- ☐ No one will ever know.
- ☐ Here's a hug.
- ☐ They don't deserve you.
- ☐ Every cloud has a silver lining.
- ☐ It was totally his fault.
- ☐ It was totally her fault.
- ☐ A rising tide lifts all boats.
- ☐ There are specialists for that.
- ☐ Think of the big picture.
- ☐ Don't let it bother you so much.
- ☐ No one saw you trip.
- ☐ You'll get that promotion soon.
- ☐ It could've been much worse.
- ☐ Aim for the stars.
- ☐ You'll forget about it, I promise.

- ☐ All publicity is good publicity.
- ☐ You can always return it.
- ☐ That was so understandable.
- ☐ You look great.
- ☐ You look great for your age.
- ☐ That happens to everyone.
- ☐ You made your point.
- ☐ Who wants that responsibility?
- ☐ It's not more than you can handle.
- ☐ Time heals all wounds.
- ☐ Time wounds all heels.
- ☐ I'm sure you don't normally do that.
- ☐ Success or not, you are loved.
- ☐ It's a journey, not a destination.
- ☐ It was a long shot anyway.
- ☐ Lesson learned.
- ☐ It's not you, it's the economy.
- ☐ You can always sue.
- ☐ You're the bigger person.
- ☐ You still have your honor.
- ☐ You still have your hair.
- ☐ Heartbreak makes you wiser.
- ☐ People will see through that.
- ☐ You'll be the last one standing.
- ☐ Don't let it get you down.
- ☐ It's not forever.
- ☐ There are always people like that.
- ☐ Never fear, karma's a bitch.
- ☐ I think it looks cute.
- ☐ One door closes, another opens.
- ☐ It's all part of the plan.
- ☐ Go ahead, cry it out.
- ☐ They spelled your name right.
- ☐ Jobs come, jobs go.
- ☐ People come, people go.
- ☐ This must be hard for you.
- ☐ Time to get on with your life.
- ☐ Everyone's a critic.
- ☐ It's for the best.
- ☐ Don't go there.
- ☐ It's their loss.
- ☐ You can focus on your career.
- ☐ You can focus on your kids.
- ☐ Didn't kill ya; made ya stronger.
- ☐ Ours is not to reason why.
- ☐ Don't take it home with you.
- ☐ Timing is everything.
- ☐ You'll eventually love it.
- ☐ Think positive.
- ☐ Think denial.

- ☐ Someday you'll understand.
- ☐ Single life is actually better.
- ☐ Always darkest before the dawn.
- ☐ Just clear the browser history.
- ☐ You're still young.
- ☐ He isn't worth it.
- ☐ She isn't worth it.
- ☐ Where there's a will . . .
- ☐ Chalk it up to experience.
- ☐ Cross that bridge later.
- ☐ One day at a time.
- ☐ You can always get it fixed.
- ☐ Don't sweat the small stuff.
- ☐ Not over 'til the fat lady sings.
- ☐ It's all nonsense anyway.
- ☐ You gotta believe in you.
- ☐ I believe in you.
- ☐ Anything is possible.
- ☐ You reacted with integrity.
- ☐ You can sell it online.
- ☐ Don't get mad, get even.
- ☐ No one can tell it's a knockoff.
- ☐ Just say no.
- ☐ Hang in there, baby.
- ☐ If it's not one thing, it's another.
- ☐ It'll build character.
- ☐ It was meant to be.
- ☐ It wasn't meant to be.
- ☐ If it's meant to be, it'll happen.
- ☐ Keep your chin up.
- ☐ You don't need their approval.
- ☐ For every hill there's a valley.
- ☐ I would've done the same.
- ☐ Life goes on.
- ☐ Absence makes love stronger.
- ☐ Can't beat 'em? Join 'em.
- ☐ Shake it off.
- ☐ No one heard it.
- ☐ Better late than never.
- ☐ Better safe than sorry.
- ☐ And so it goes.
- ☐ The first cut is the deepest.
- ☐ Love hurts.
- ☐ Love stinks.
- ☐ Love is overrated.
- ☐ Soon this'll be a distant memory.
- ☐ Keep on truckin'.
- ☐ Quit worrying.
- ☐ It's water under the bridge.
- ☐ Don't dwell on it.

- ☐ Ya gotta do what ya gotta do.
- ☐ When it rains, it pours.
- ☐ Every rose has a thorn.
- ☐ You gave it your best shot.
- ☐ There, there.
- ☐ It takes all kinds.
- ☐ They're just jealous.
- ☐ It'll come when you're ready.
- ☐ Nobody mentioned it.
- ☐ Try to keep it in perspective.
- ☐ Put on your big girl panties.
- ☐ Put on your big boy briefs.
- ☐ There's a lid for every pot.
- ☐ He's probably out of town.
- ☐ Her phone is probably dead.
- ☐ You're better off.
- ☐ It happens sometimes.
- ☐ They don't understand you.
- ☐ It was an honest mistake.
- ☐ Money can't buy love.
- ☐ Adversity forges character.
- ☐ You'll feel better after a bath.
- ☐ You'll feel better after a drink.
- ☐ It'll make great memoir material.
- ☐ Quit blaming yourself.
- ☐ There's no such thing as normal.
- ☐ You'll show them.
- ☐ This will forge your character.
- ☐ You're a superstar.
- ☐ Just explain what happened.
- ☐ Don't compare.
- ☐ All parents screw up.
- ☐ All kids screw up.
- ☐ At least you have your health.
- ☐ He'll grow out of it.
- ☐ She'll grow out of it.
- ☐ Shhh. Shhh. It's okay now.
- ☐ Pain is temporary.
- ☐ I agree with you.
- ☐ One day you'll know why.
- ☐ You march to your own beat.
- ☐ Ignore what others think.
- ☐ Buck up, buckwheat.
- ☐ Everyone sympathizes.
- ☐ You're overthinking this.
- ☐ Get back up on the horse.
- ☐ Just give it some time.
- ☐ It's not the end of the world.
- ☐ It gets better.
- ☐ Really, it is.

☐ **TOTALLY OKAY** ☐ **PRETTY OKAY** ☐ **OKAY-ISH**

SIGNATURE	MONTH	DAY	YEAR

"OKAY? OKAY. OKAY!"

IT'S GONNA BE OKAY

☐ RIGHT NOW ☐ FAIRLY SOON ☐ EVENTUALLY

- ☐ It'll grow back.
- ☐ You'll get over it.
- ☐ You can do this.
- ☐ It wasn't that obvious.
- ☐ This too shall pass.
- ☐ You're too good for him.
- ☐ You're too good for her.
- ☐ I'll never tell.
- ☐ Don't blame yourself.
- ☐ There are other fish in the sea.
- ☐ Tattoo removal is easier now.
- ☐ You are not your job.
- ☐ Your mother will never know.
- ☐ Nothing therapy won't cure.
- ☐ Just take a mulligan.
- ☐ Moving home is no big deal.
- ☐ Don't "should" all over yourself.
- ☐ At least you know you're right.
- ☐ You did your best.
- ☐ Can't win 'em all.
- ☐ You couldn't have known.
- ☐ My cousin had that and was fine.
- ☐ Laughter is the best medicine.
- ☐ Have faith.
- ☐ Penicillin clears that up fast.
- ☐ He wasn't thinking.
- ☐ She wasn't thinking.
- ☐ If at first you don't succeed . . .
- ☐ It's about quality, not quantity.
- ☐ That's not old, it's vintage.
- ☐ You're not old, you're vintage.
- ☐ Things happen for a reason.
- ☐ It'll look better in the morning.
- ☐ You can blog about it.
- ☐ We'll look back later and laugh.
- ☐ No one will ever know.
- ☐ Here's a hug.
- ☐ They don't deserve you.
- ☐ Every cloud has a silver lining.
- ☐ It was totally his fault.
- ☐ It was totally her fault.
- ☐ A rising tide lifts all boats.
- ☐ There are specialists for that.
- ☐ Think of the big picture.
- ☐ Don't let it bother you so much.
- ☐ No one saw you trip.
- ☐ You'll get that promotion soon.
- ☐ It could've been much worse.
- ☐ Aim for the stars.
- ☐ You'll forget about it, I promise.
- ☐ All publicity is good publicity.
- ☐ You can always return it.
- ☐ That was so understandable.
- ☐ You look great.
- ☐ You look great for your age.
- ☐ That happens to everyone.
- ☐ You made your point.
- ☐ Who wants that responsibility?
- ☐ It's not more than you can handle.
- ☐ Time heals all wounds.
- ☐ Time wounds all heels.
- ☐ I'm sure you don't normally do that.
- ☐ Success or not, you are loved.
- ☐ It's a journey, not a destination.
- ☐ It was a long shot anyway.
- ☐ Lesson learned.
- ☐ It's not you, it's the economy.
- ☐ You can always sue.
- ☐ You're the bigger person.
- ☐ You still have your honor.
- ☐ You still have your hair.
- ☐ Heartbreak makes you wiser.
- ☐ People will see through that.
- ☐ You'll be the last one standing.
- ☐ Don't let it get you down.
- ☐ It's not forever.
- ☐ There are always people like that.
- ☐ Never fear, karma's a bitch.
- ☐ I think it looks cute.
- ☐ One door closes, another opens.
- ☐ It's all part of the plan.
- ☐ Go ahead, cry it out.
- ☐ They spelled your name right.
- ☐ Jobs come, jobs go.
- ☐ People come, people go.
- ☐ This must be hard for you.
- ☐ Time to get on with your life.
- ☐ Everyone's a critic.
- ☐ It's for the best.
- ☐ Don't go there.
- ☐ It's their loss.
- ☐ You can focus on your career.
- ☐ You can focus on your kids.
- ☐ Didn't kill ya; made ya stronger.
- ☐ Ours is not to reason why.
- ☐ Don't take it home with you.
- ☐ Timing is everything.
- ☐ You'll eventually love it.
- ☐ Think positive.
- ☐ Think denial.
- ☐ Someday you'll understand.
- ☐ Single life is actually better.
- ☐ Always darkest before the dawn.
- ☐ Just clear the browser history.
- ☐ You're still young.
- ☐ He isn't worth it.
- ☐ She isn't worth it.
- ☐ Where there's a will . . .
- ☐ Chalk it up to experience.
- ☐ Cross that bridge later.
- ☐ One day at a time.
- ☐ You can always get it fixed.
- ☐ Don't sweat the small stuff.
- ☐ Not over 'til the fat lady sings.
- ☐ It's all nonsense anyway.
- ☐ You gotta believe in you.
- ☐ I believe in you.
- ☐ Anything is possible.
- ☐ You reacted with integrity.
- ☐ You can sell it online.
- ☐ Don't get mad, get even.
- ☐ No one can tell it's a knockoff.
- ☐ Just say no.
- ☐ Hang in there, baby.
- ☐ If it's not one thing, it's another.
- ☐ It'll build character.
- ☐ It was meant to be.
- ☐ It wasn't meant to be.
- ☐ If it's meant to be, it'll happen.
- ☐ Keep your chin up.
- ☐ You don't need their approval.
- ☐ For every hill there's a valley.
- ☐ I would've done the same.
- ☐ Life goes on.
- ☐ Absence makes love stronger.
- ☐ Can't beat 'em? Join 'em.
- ☐ Shake it off.
- ☐ No one heard it.
- ☐ Better late than never.
- ☐ Better safe than sorry.
- ☐ And so it goes.
- ☐ The first cut is the deepest.
- ☐ Love hurts.
- ☐ Love stinks.
- ☐ Love is overrated.
- ☐ Soon this'll be a distant memory.
- ☐ Keep on truckin'.
- ☐ Quit worrying.
- ☐ It's water under the bridge.
- ☐ Don't dwell on it.
- ☐ Ya gotta do what ya gotta do.
- ☐ When it rains, it pours.
- ☐ Every rose has a thorn.
- ☐ You gave it your best shot.
- ☐ There, there.
- ☐ It takes all kinds.
- ☐ They're just jealous.
- ☐ It'll come when you're ready.
- ☐ Nobody mentioned it.
- ☐ Try to keep it in perspective.
- ☐ Put on your big girl panties.
- ☐ Put on your big boy briefs.
- ☐ There's a lid for every pot.
- ☐ He's probably out of town.
- ☐ Her phone is probably dead.
- ☐ You're better off.
- ☐ It happens sometimes.
- ☐ They don't understand you.
- ☐ It was an honest mistake.
- ☐ Money can't buy love.
- ☐ Adversity forges character.
- ☐ You'll feel better after a bath.
- ☐ You'll feel better after a drink.
- ☐ It'll make great memoir material.
- ☐ Quit blaming yourself.
- ☐ There's no such thing as normal.
- ☐ You'll show them.
- ☐ This will forge your character.
- ☐ You're a superstar.
- ☐ Just explain what happened.
- ☐ Don't compare.
- ☐ All parents screw up.
- ☐ All kids screw up.
- ☐ At least you have your health.
- ☐ He'll grow out of it.
- ☐ She'll grow out of it.
- ☐ Shhh. Shhh. It's okay now.
- ☐ Pain is temporary.
- ☐ I agree with you.
- ☐ One day you'll know why.
- ☐ You march to your own beat.
- ☐ Ignore what others think.
- ☐ Buck up, buckwheat.
- ☐ Everyone sympathizes.
- ☐ You're overthinking this.
- ☐ Get back up on the horse.
- ☐ Just give it some time.
- ☐ It's not the end of the world.
- ☐ It gets better.
- ☐ Really, it is.

☐ TOTALLY OKAY ☐ PRETTY OKAY ☐ OKAY-ISH

SIGNATURE	MONTH	DAY	YEAR

"OKAY? OKAY. OKAY!"

IT'S GONNA BE OKAY

☐ RIGHT NOW ☐ FAIRLY SOON ☐ EVENTUALLY

- ☐ It'll grow back.
- ☐ You'll get over it.
- ☐ You can do this.
- ☐ It wasn't that obvious.
- ☐ This too shall pass.
- ☐ You're too good for him.
- ☐ You're too good for her.
- ☐ I'll never tell.
- ☐ Don't blame yourself.
- ☐ There are other fish in the sea.
- ☐ Tattoo removal is easier now.
- ☐ You are not your job.
- ☐ Your mother will never know.
- ☐ Nothing therapy won't cure.
- ☐ Just take a mulligan.
- ☐ Moving home is no big deal.
- ☐ Don't "should" all over yourself.
- ☐ At least you know you're right.
- ☐ You did your best.
- ☐ Can't win 'em all.
- ☐ You couldn't have known.
- ☐ My cousin had that and was fine.
- ☐ Laughter is the best medicine.
- ☐ Have faith.
- ☐ Penicillin clears that up fast.
- ☐ He wasn't thinking.
- ☐ She wasn't thinking.
- ☐ If at first you don't succeed . . .
- ☐ It's about quality, not quantity.
- ☐ That's not old, it's vintage.
- ☐ You're not old, you're vintage.
- ☐ Things happen for a reason.
- ☐ It'll look better in the morning.
- ☐ You can blog about it.
- ☐ We'll look back later and laugh.
- ☐ No one will ever know.
- ☐ Here's a hug.
- ☐ They don't deserve you.
- ☐ Every cloud has a silver lining.
- ☐ It was totally his fault.
- ☐ It was totally her fault.
- ☐ A rising tide lifts all boats.
- ☐ There are specialists for that.
- ☐ Think of the big picture.
- ☐ Don't let it bother you so much.
- ☐ No one saw you trip.
- ☐ You'll get that promotion soon.
- ☐ It could've been much worse.
- ☐ Aim for the stars.
- ☐ You'll forget about it, I promise.

- ☐ All publicity is good publicity.
- ☐ You can always return it.
- ☐ That was so understandable.
- ☐ You look great.
- ☐ You look great for your age.
- ☐ That happens to everyone.
- ☐ You made your point.
- ☐ Who wants that responsibility?
- ☐ It's not more than you can handle.
- ☐ Time heals all wounds.
- ☐ Time wounds all heels.
- ☐ I'm sure you don't normally do that.
- ☐ Success or not, you are loved.
- ☐ It's a journey, not a destination.
- ☐ It was a long shot anyway.
- ☐ Lesson learned.
- ☐ It's not you, it's the economy.
- ☐ You can always sue.
- ☐ You're the bigger person.
- ☐ You still have your honor.
- ☐ You still have your hair.
- ☐ Heartbreak makes you wiser.
- ☐ People will see through that.
- ☐ You'll be the last one standing.
- ☐ Don't let it get you down.
- ☐ It's not forever.
- ☐ There are always people like that.
- ☐ Never fear, karma's a bitch.
- ☐ I think it looks cute.
- ☐ One door closes, another opens.
- ☐ It's all part of the plan.
- ☐ Go ahead, cry it out.
- ☐ They spelled your name right.
- ☐ Jobs come, jobs go.
- ☐ People come, people go.
- ☐ This must be hard for you.
- ☐ Time to get on with your life.
- ☐ Everyone's a critic.
- ☐ It's for the best.
- ☐ Don't go there.
- ☐ It's their loss.
- ☐ You can focus on your career.
- ☐ You can focus on your kids.
- ☐ Didn't kill ya; made ya stronger.
- ☐ Ours is not to reason why.
- ☐ Don't take it home with you.
- ☐ Timing is everything.
- ☐ You'll eventually love it.
- ☐ Think positive.
- ☐ Think denial.

- ☐ Someday you'll understand.
- ☐ Single life is actually better.
- ☐ Always darkest before the dawn.
- ☐ Just clear the browser history.
- ☐ You're still young.
- ☐ He isn't worth it.
- ☐ She isn't worth it.
- ☐ Where there's a will . . .
- ☐ Chalk it up to experience.
- ☐ Cross that bridge later.
- ☐ One day at a time.
- ☐ You can always get it fixed.
- ☐ Don't sweat the small stuff.
- ☐ Not over 'til the fat lady sings.
- ☐ It's all nonsense anyway.
- ☐ You gotta believe in you.
- ☐ I believe in you.
- ☐ Anything is possible.
- ☐ You reacted with integrity.
- ☐ You can sell it online.
- ☐ Don't get mad, get even.
- ☐ No one can tell it's a knockoff.
- ☐ Just say no.
- ☐ Hang in there, baby.
- ☐ If it's not one thing, it's another.
- ☐ It'll build character.
- ☐ It was meant to be.
- ☐ It wasn't meant to be.
- ☐ If it's meant to be, it'll happen.
- ☐ Keep your chin up.
- ☐ You don't need their approval.
- ☐ For every hill there's a valley.
- ☐ I would've done the same.
- ☐ Life goes on.
- ☐ Absence makes love stronger.
- ☐ Can't beat 'em? Join 'em.
- ☐ Shake it off.
- ☐ No one heard it.
- ☐ Better late than never.
- ☐ Better safe than sorry.
- ☐ And so it goes.
- ☐ The first cut is the deepest.
- ☐ Love hurts.
- ☐ Love stinks.
- ☐ Love is overrated.
- ☐ Soon this'll be a distant memory.
- ☐ Keep on truckin'.
- ☐ Quit worrying.
- ☐ It's water under the bridge.
- ☐ Don't dwell on it.

- ☐ Ya gotta do what ya gotta do.
- ☐ When it rains, it pours.
- ☐ Every rose has a thorn.
- ☐ You gave it your best shot.
- ☐ There, there.
- ☐ It takes all kinds.
- ☐ They're just jealous.
- ☐ It'll come when you're ready.
- ☐ Nobody mentioned it.
- ☐ Try to keep it in perspective.
- ☐ Put on your big girl panties.
- ☐ Put on your big boy briefs.
- ☐ There's a lid for every pot.
- ☐ He's probably out of town.
- ☐ Her phone is probably dead.
- ☐ You're better off.
- ☐ It happens sometimes.
- ☐ They don't understand you.
- ☐ It was an honest mistake.
- ☐ Money can't buy love.
- ☐ Adversity forges character.
- ☐ You'll feel better after a bath.
- ☐ You'll feel better after a drink.
- ☐ It'll make great memoir material.
- ☐ Quit blaming yourself.
- ☐ There's no such thing as normal.
- ☐ You'll show them.
- ☐ This will forge your character.
- ☐ You're a superstar.
- ☐ Just explain what happened.
- ☐ Don't compare.
- ☐ All parents screw up.
- ☐ All kids screw up.
- ☐ At least you have your health.
- ☐ He'll grow out of it.
- ☐ She'll grow out of it.
- ☐ Shhh. Shhh. It's okay now.
- ☐ Pain is temporary.
- ☐ I agree with you.
- ☐ One day you'll know why.
- ☐ You march to your own beat.
- ☐ Ignore what others think.
- ☐ Buck up, buckwheat.
- ☐ Everyone sympathizes.
- ☐ You're overthinking this.
- ☐ Get back up on the horse.
- ☐ Just give it some time.
- ☐ It's not the end of the world.
- ☐ It gets better.
- ☐ Really, it is.

☐ TOTALLY OKAY ☐ PRETTY OKAY ☐ OKAY-ISH

SIGNATURE MONTH DAY YEAR

"OKAY? OKAY. OKAY!"

IT'S GONNA BE OKAY

☐ **RIGHT NOW** ☐ **FAIRLY SOON** ☐ **EVENTUALLY**

☐ It'll grow back.
☐ You'll get over it.
☐ You can do this.
☐ It wasn't that obvious.
☐ This too shall pass.
☐ You're too good for him.
☐ You're too good for her.
☐ I'll never tell.
☐ Don't blame yourself.
☐ There are other fish in the sea.
☐ Tattoo removal is easier now.
☐ You are not your job.
☐ Your mother will never know.
☐ Nothing therapy won't cure.
☐ Just take a mulligan.
☐ Moving home is no big deal.
☐ Don't "should" all over yourself.
☐ At least you know you're right.
☐ You did your best.
☐ Can't win 'em all.
☐ You couldn't have known.
☐ My cousin had that and was fine.
☐ Laughter is the best medicine.
☐ Have faith.
☐ Penicillin clears that up fast.
☐ He wasn't thinking.
☐ She wasn't thinking.
☐ If at first you don't succeed . . .
☐ It's about quality, not quantity.
☐ That's not old, it's vintage.
☐ You're not old, you're vintage.
☐ Things happen for a reason.
☐ It'll look better in the morning.
☐ You can blog about it.
☐ We'll look back later and laugh.
☐ No one will ever know.
☐ Here's a hug.
☐ They don't deserve you.
☐ Every cloud has a silver lining.
☐ It was totally his fault.
☐ It was totally her fault.
☐ A rising tide lifts all boats.
☐ There are specialists for that.
☐ Think of the big picture.
☐ Don't let it bother you so much.
☐ No one saw you trip.
☐ You'll get that promotion soon.
☐ It could've been much worse.
☐ Aim for the stars.
☐ You'll forget about it, I promise.

☐ All publicity is good publicity.
☐ You can always return it.
☐ That was so understandable.
☐ You look great.
☐ You look great for your age.
☐ That happens to everyone.
☐ You made your point.
☐ Who wants that responsibility?
☐ It's not more than you can handle.
☐ Time heals all wounds.
☐ Time wounds all heels.
☐ I'm sure you don't normally do that.
☐ Success or not, you are loved.
☐ It's a journey, not a destination.
☐ It was a long shot anyway.
☐ Lesson learned.
☐ It's not you, it's the economy.
☐ You can always sue.
☐ You're the bigger person.
☐ You still have your honor.
☐ You still have your hair.
☐ Heartbreak makes you wiser.
☐ People will see through that.
☐ You'll be the last one standing.
☐ Don't let it get you down.
☐ It's not forever.
☐ There are always people like that.
☐ Never fear, karma's a bitch.
☐ I think it looks cute.
☐ One door closes, another opens.
☐ It's all part of the plan.
☐ Go ahead, cry it out.
☐ They spelled your name right.
☐ Jobs come, jobs go.
☐ People come, people go.
☐ This must be hard for you.
☐ Time to get on with your life.
☐ Everyone's a critic.
☐ It's for the best.
☐ Don't go there.
☐ It's their loss.
☐ You can focus on your career.
☐ You can focus on your kids.
☐ Didn't kill ya; made ya stronger.
☐ Ours is not to reason why.
☐ Don't take it home with you.
☐ Timing is everything.
☐ You'll eventually love it.
☐ Think positive.
☐ Think denial.

☐ Someday you'll understand.
☐ Single life is actually better.
☐ Always darkest before the dawn.
☐ Just clear the browser history.
☐ You're still young.
☐ He isn't worth it.
☐ She isn't worth it.
☐ Where there's a will . . .
☐ Chalk it up to experience.
☐ Cross that bridge later.
☐ One day at a time.
☐ You can always get it fixed.
☐ Don't sweat the small stuff.
☐ Not over 'til the fat lady sings.
☐ It's all nonsense anyway.
☐ You gotta believe in you.
☐ I believe in you.
☐ Anything is possible.
☐ You reacted with integrity.
☐ You can sell it online.
☐ Don't get mad, get even.
☐ No one can tell it's a knockoff.
☐ Just say no.
☐ Hang in there, baby.
☐ If it's not one thing, it's another.
☐ It'll build character.
☐ It was meant to be.
☐ It wasn't meant to be.
☐ If it's meant to be, it'll happen.
☐ Keep your chin up.
☐ You don't need their approval.
☐ For every hill there's a valley.
☐ I would've done the same.
☐ Life goes on.
☐ Absence makes love stronger.
☐ Can't beat 'em? Join 'em.
☐ Shake it off.
☐ No one heard it.
☐ Better late than never.
☐ Better safe than sorry.
☐ And so it goes.
☐ The first cut is the deepest.
☐ Love hurts.
☐ Love stinks.
☐ Love is overrated.
☐ Soon this'll be a distant memory.
☐ Keep on truckin'.
☐ Quit worrying.
☐ It's water under the bridge.
☐ Don't dwell on it.

☐ Ya gotta do what ya gotta do.
☐ When it rains, it pours.
☐ Every rose has a thorn.
☐ You gave it your best shot.
☐ There, there.
☐ It takes all kinds.
☐ They're just jealous.
☐ It'll come when you're ready.
☐ Nobody mentioned it.
☐ Try to keep it in perspective.
☐ Put on your big girl panties.
☐ Put on your big boy briefs.
☐ There's a lid for every pot.
☐ He's probably out of town.
☐ Her phone is probably dead.
☐ You're better off.
☐ It happens sometimes.
☐ They don't understand you.
☐ It was an honest mistake.
☐ Money can't buy love.
☐ Adversity forges character.
☐ You'll feel better after a bath.
☐ You'll feel better after a drink.
☐ It'll make great memoir material.
☐ Quit blaming yourself.
☐ There's no such thing as normal.
☐ You'll show them.
☐ This will forge your character.
☐ You're a superstar.
☐ Just explain what happened.
☐ Don't compare.
☐ All parents screw up.
☐ All kids screw up.
☐ At least you have your health.
☐ He'll grow out of it.
☐ She'll grow out of it.
☐ Shhh. Shhh. It's okay now.
☐ Pain is temporary.
☐ I agree with you.
☐ One day you'll know why.
☐ You march to your own beat.
☐ Ignore what others think.
☐ Buck up, buckwheat.
☐ Everyone sympathizes.
☐ You're overthinking this.
☐ Get back up on the horse.
☐ Just give it some time.
☐ It's not the end of the world.
☐ It gets better.
☐ Really, it is.

☐ **TOTALLY OKAY** ☐ **PRETTY OKAY** ☐ **OKAY-ISH**

SIGNATURE

MONTH | DAY | YEAR

"OKAY? OKAY. OKAY!"

IT'S GONNA BE OKAY

☐ **RIGHT NOW** ☐ **FAIRLY SOON** ☐ **EVENTUALLY**

☐ It'll grow back.
☐ You'll get over it.
☐ You can do this.
☐ It wasn't that obvious.
☐ This too shall pass.
☐ You're too good for him.
☐ You're too good for her.
☐ I'll never tell.
☐ Don't blame yourself.
☐ There are other fish in the sea.
☐ Tattoo removal is easier now.
☐ You are not your job.
☐ Your mother will never know.
☐ Nothing therapy won't cure.
☐ Just take a mulligan.
☐ Moving home is no big deal.
☐ Don't "should" all over yourself.
☐ At least you know you're right.
☐ You did your best.
☐ Can't win 'em all.
☐ You couldn't have known.
☐ My cousin had that and was fine.
☐ Laughter is the best medicine.
☐ Have faith.
☐ Penicillin clears that up fast.
☐ He wasn't thinking.
☐ She wasn't thinking.
☐ If at first you don't succeed . . .
☐ It's about quality, not quantity.
☐ That's not old, it's vintage.
☐ You're not old, you're vintage.
☐ Things happen for a reason.
☐ It'll look better in the morning.
☐ You can blog about it.
☐ We'll look back later and laugh.
☐ No one will ever know.
☐ Here's a hug.
☐ They don't deserve you.
☐ Every cloud has a silver lining.
☐ It was totally his fault.
☐ It was totally her fault.
☐ A rising tide lifts all boats.
☐ There are specialists for that.
☐ Think of the big picture.
☐ Don't let it bother you so much.
☐ No one saw you trip.
☐ You'll get that promotion soon.
☐ It could've been much worse.
☐ Aim for the stars.
☐ You'll forget about it, I promise.

☐ All publicity is good publicity.
☐ You can always return it.
☐ That was so understandable.
☐ You look great.
☐ You look great for your age.
☐ That happens to everyone.
☐ You made your point.
☐ Who wants that responsibility?
☐ It's not more than you can handle.
☐ Time heals all wounds.
☐ Time wounds all heels.
☐ I'm sure you don't normally do that.
☐ Success or not, you are loved.
☐ It's a journey, not a destination.
☐ It was a long shot anyway.
☐ Lesson learned.
☐ It's not you, it's the economy.
☐ You can always sue.
☐ You're the bigger person.
☐ You still have your honor.
☐ You still have your hair.
☐ Heartbreak makes you wiser.
☐ People will see through that.
☐ You'll be the last one standing.
☐ Don't let it get you down.
☐ It's not forever.
☐ There are always people like that.
☐ Never fear, karma's a bitch.
☐ I think it looks cute.
☐ One door closes, another opens.
☐ It's all part of the plan.
☐ Go ahead, cry it out.
☐ They spelled your name right.
☐ Jobs come, jobs go.
☐ People come, people go.
☐ This must be hard for you.
☐ Time to get on with your life.
☐ Everyone's a critic.
☐ It's for the best.
☐ Don't go there.
☐ It's their loss.
☐ You can focus on your career.
☐ You can focus on your kids.
☐ Didn't kill ya; made ya stronger.
☐ Ours is not to reason why.
☐ Don't take it home with you.
☐ Timing is everything.
☐ You'll eventually love it.
☐ Think positive.
☐ Think denial.

☐ Someday you'll understand.
☐ Single life is actually better.
☐ Always darkest before the dawn.
☐ Just clear the browser history.
☐ You're still young.
☐ He isn't worth it.
☐ She isn't worth it.
☐ Where there's a will . . .
☐ Chalk it up to experience.
☐ Cross that bridge later.
☐ One day at a time.
☐ You can always get it fixed.
☐ Don't sweat the small stuff.
☐ Not over 'til the fat lady sings.
☐ It's all nonsense anyway.
☐ You gotta believe in you.
☐ I believe in you.
☐ Anything is possible.
☐ You reacted with integrity.
☐ You can sell it online.
☐ Don't get mad, get even.
☐ No one can tell it's a knockoff.
☐ Just say no.
☐ Hang in there, baby.
☐ If it's not one thing, it's another.
☐ It'll build character.
☐ It was meant to be.
☐ It wasn't meant to be.
☐ If it's meant to be, it'll happen.
☐ Keep your chin up.
☐ You don't need their approval.
☐ For every hill there's a valley.
☐ I would've done the same.
☐ Life goes on.
☐ Absence makes love stronger.
☐ Can't beat 'em? Join 'em.
☐ Shake it off.
☐ No one heard it.
☐ Better late than never.
☐ Better safe than sorry.
☐ And so it goes.
☐ The first cut is the deepest.
☐ Love hurts.
☐ Love stinks.
☐ Love is overrated.
☐ Soon this'll be a distant memory.
☐ Keep on truckin'.
☐ Quit worrying.
☐ It's water under the bridge.
☐ Don't dwell on it.

☐ Ya gotta do what ya gotta do.
☐ When it rains, it pours.
☐ Every rose has a thorn.
☐ You gave it your best shot.
☐ There, there.
☐ It takes all kinds.
☐ They're just jealous.
☐ It'll come when you're ready.
☐ Nobody mentioned it.
☐ Try to keep it in perspective.
☐ Put on your big girl panties.
☐ Put on your big boy briefs.
☐ There's a lid for every pot.
☐ He's probably out of town.
☐ Her phone is probably dead.
☐ You're better off.
☐ It happens sometimes.
☐ They don't understand you.
☐ It was an honest mistake.
☐ Money can't buy love.
☐ Adversity forges character.
☐ You'll feel better after a bath.
☐ You'll feel better after a drink.
☐ It'll make great memoir material.
☐ Quit blaming yourself.
☐ There's no such thing as normal.
☐ You'll show them.
☐ This will forge your character.
☐ You're a superstar.
☐ Just explain what happened.
☐ Don't compare.
☐ All parents screw up.
☐ All kids screw up.
☐ At least you have your health.
☐ He'll grow out of it.
☐ She'll grow out of it.
☐ Shhh. Shhh. It's okay now.
☐ Pain is temporary.
☐ I agree with you.
☐ One day you'll know why.
☐ You march to your own beat.
☐ Ignore what others think.
☐ Buck up, buckwheat.
☐ Everyone sympathizes.
☐ You're overthinking this.
☐ Get back up on the horse.
☐ Just give it some time.
☐ It's not the end of the world.
☐ It gets better.
☐ Really, it is.

☐ **TOTALLY OKAY** ☐ **PRETTY OKAY** ☐ **OKAY-ISH**

SIGNATURE MONTH DAY YEAR

"OKAY? OKAY. OKAY!"

IT'S GONNA BE OKAY

☐ **RIGHT NOW** ☐ **FAIRLY SOON** ☐ **EVENTUALLY**

☐ It'll grow back.
☐ You'll get over it.
☐ You can do this.
☐ It wasn't that obvious.
☐ This too shall pass.
☐ You're too good for him.
☐ You're too good for her.
☐ I'll never tell.
☐ Don't blame yourself.
☐ There are other fish in the sea.
☐ Tattoo removal is easier now.
☐ You are not your job.
☐ Your mother will never know.
☐ Nothing therapy won't cure.
☐ Just take a mulligan.
☐ Moving home is no big deal.
☐ Don't "should" all over yourself.
☐ At least you know you're right.
☐ You did your best.
☐ Can't win 'em all.
☐ You couldn't have known.
☐ My cousin had that and was fine.
☐ Laughter is the best medicine.
☐ Have faith.
☐ Penicillin clears that up fast.
☐ He wasn't thinking.
☐ She wasn't thinking.
☐ If at first you don't succeed . . .
☐ It's about quality, not quantity.
☐ That's not old, it's vintage.
☐ You're not old, you're vintage.
☐ Things happen for a reason.
☐ It'll look better in the morning.
☐ You can blog about it.
☐ We'll look back later and laugh.
☐ No one will ever know.
☐ Here's a hug.
☐ They don't deserve you.
☐ Every cloud has a silver lining.
☐ It was totally his fault.
☐ It was totally her fault.
☐ A rising tide lifts all boats.
☐ There are specialists for that.
☐ Think of the big picture.
☐ Don't let it bother you so much.
☐ No one saw you trip.
☐ You'll get that promotion soon.
☐ It could've been much worse.
☐ Aim for the stars.
☐ You'll forget about it, I promise.

☐ All publicity is good publicity.
☐ You can always return it.
☐ That was so understandable.
☐ You look great.
☐ You look great for your age.
☐ That happens to everyone.
☐ You made your point.
☐ Who wants that responsibility?
☐ It's not more than you can handle.
☐ Time heals all wounds.
☐ Time wounds all heels.
☐ I'm sure you don't normally do that.
☐ Success or not, you are loved.
☐ It's a journey, not a destination.
☐ It was a long shot anyway.
☐ Lesson learned.
☐ It's not you, it's the economy.
☐ You can always sue.
☐ You're the bigger person.
☐ You still have your honor.
☐ You still have your hair.
☐ Heartbreak makes you wiser.
☐ People will see through that.
☐ You'll be the last one standing.
☐ Don't let it get you down.
☐ It's not forever.
☐ There are always people like that.
☐ Never fear, karma's a bitch.
☐ I think it looks cute.
☐ One door closes, another opens.
☐ It's all part of the plan.
☐ Go ahead, cry it out.
☐ They spelled your name right.
☐ Jobs come, jobs go.
☐ People come, people go.
☐ This must be hard for you.
☐ Time to get on with your life.
☐ Everyone's a critic.
☐ It's for the best.
☐ Don't go there.
☐ It's their loss.
☐ You can focus on your career.
☐ You can focus on your kids.
☐ Didn't kill ya; made ya stronger.
☐ Ours is not to reason why.
☐ Don't take it home with you.
☐ Timing is everything.
☐ You'll eventually love it.
☐ Think positive.
☐ Think denial.

☐ Someday you'll understand.
☐ Single life is actually better.
☐ Always darkest before the dawn.
☐ Just clear the browser history.
☐ You're still young.
☐ He isn't worth it.
☐ She isn't worth it.
☐ Where there's a will . . .
☐ Chalk it up to experience.
☐ Cross that bridge later.
☐ One day at a time.
☐ You can always get it fixed.
☐ Don't sweat the small stuff.
☐ Not over 'til the fat lady sings.
☐ It's all nonsense anyway.
☐ You gotta believe in you.
☐ I believe in you.
☐ Anything is possible.
☐ You reacted with integrity.
☐ You can sell it online.
☐ Don't get mad, get even.
☐ No one can tell it's a knockoff.
☐ Just say no.
☐ Hang in there, baby.
☐ If it's not one thing, it's another.
☐ It'll build character.
☐ It was meant to be.
☐ It wasn't meant to be.
☐ If it's meant to be, it'll happen.
☐ Keep your chin up.
☐ You don't need their approval.
☐ For every hill there's a valley.
☐ I would've done the same.
☐ Life goes on.
☐ Absence makes love stronger.
☐ Can't beat 'em? Join 'em.
☐ Shake it off.
☐ No one heard it.
☐ Better late than never.
☐ Better safe than sorry.
☐ And so it goes.
☐ The first cut is the deepest.
☐ Love hurts.
☐ Love stinks.
☐ Love is overrated.
☐ Soon this'll be a distant memory.
☐ Keep on truckin'.
☐ Quit worrying.
☐ It's water under the bridge.
☐ Don't dwell on it.

☐ Ya gotta do what ya gotta do.
☐ When it rains, it pours.
☐ Every rose has a thorn.
☐ You gave it your best shot.
☐ There, there.
☐ It takes all kinds.
☐ They're just jealous.
☐ It'll come when you're ready.
☐ Nobody mentioned it.
☐ Try to keep it in perspective.
☐ Put on your big girl panties.
☐ Put on your big boy briefs.
☐ There's a lid for every pot.
☐ He's probably out of town.
☐ Her phone is probably dead.
☐ You're better off.
☐ It happens sometimes.
☐ They don't understand you.
☐ It was an honest mistake.
☐ Money can't buy love.
☐ Adversity forges character.
☐ You'll feel better after a bath.
☐ You'll feel better after a drink.
☐ It'll make great memoir material.
☐ Quit blaming yourself.
☐ There's no such thing as normal.
☐ You'll show them.
☐ This will forge your character.
☐ You're a superstar.
☐ Just explain what happened.
☐ Don't compare.
☐ All parents screw up.
☐ All kids screw up.
☐ At least you have your health.
☐ He'll grow out of it.
☐ She'll grow out of it.
☐ Shhh. Shhh. It's okay now.
☐ Pain is temporary.
☐ I agree with you.
☐ One day you'll know why.
☐ You march to your own beat.
☐ Ignore what others think.
☐ Buck up, buckwheat.
☐ Everyone sympathizes.
☐ You're overthinking this.
☐ Get back up on the horse.
☐ Just give it some time.
☐ It's not the end of the world.
☐ It gets better.
☐ Really, it is.

☐ **TOTALLY OKAY** ☐ **PRETTY OKAY** ☐ **OKAY-ISH**

SIGNATURE MONTH DAY YEAR

"OKAY? OKAY. OKAY!"

IT'S GONNA BE OKAY

☐ **RIGHT NOW** ☐ **FAIRLY SOON** ☐ **EVENTUALLY**

☐ It'll grow back.
☐ You'll get over it.
☐ You can do this.
☐ It wasn't that obvious.
☐ This too shall pass.
☐ You're too good for him.
☐ You're too good for her.
☐ I'll never tell.
☐ Don't blame yourself.
☐ There are other fish in the sea.
☐ Tattoo removal is easier now.
☐ You are not your job.
☐ Your mother will never know.
☐ Nothing therapy won't cure.
☐ Just take a mulligan.
☐ Moving home is no big deal.
☐ Don't "should" all over yourself.
☐ At least you know you're right.
☐ You did your best.
☐ Can't win 'em all.
☐ You couldn't have known.
☐ My cousin had that and was fine.
☐ Laughter is the best medicine.
☐ Have faith.
☐ Penicillin clears that up fast.
☐ He wasn't thinking.
☐ She wasn't thinking.
☐ If at first you don't succeed . . .
☐ It's about quality, not quantity.
☐ That's not old, it's vintage.
☐ You're not old, you're vintage.
☐ Things happen for a reason.
☐ It'll look better in the morning.
☐ You can blog about it.
☐ We'll look back later and laugh.
☐ No one will ever know.
☐ Here's a hug.
☐ They don't deserve you.
☐ Every cloud has a silver lining.
☐ It was totally his fault.
☐ It was totally her fault.
☐ A rising tide lifts all boats.
☐ There are specialists for that.
☐ Think of the big picture.
☐ Don't let it bother you so much.
☐ No one saw you trip.
☐ You'll get that promotion soon.
☐ It could've been much worse.
☐ Aim for the stars.
☐ You'll forget about it, I promise.

☐ All publicity is good publicity.
☐ You can always return it.
☐ That was so understandable.
☐ You look great.
☐ You look great for your age.
☐ That happens to everyone.
☐ You made your point.
☐ Who wants that responsibility?
☐ It's not more than you can handle.
☐ Time heals all wounds.
☐ Time wounds all heels.
☐ I'm sure you don't normally do that.
☐ Success or not, you are loved.
☐ It's a journey, not a destination.
☐ It was a long shot anyway.
☐ Lesson learned.
☐ It's not you, it's the economy.
☐ You can always sue.
☐ You're the bigger person.
☐ You still have your honor.
☐ You still have your hair.
☐ Heartbreak makes you wiser.
☐ People will see through that.
☐ You'll be the last one standing.
☐ Don't let it get you down.
☐ It's not forever.
☐ There are always people like that.
☐ Never fear, karma's a bitch.
☐ I think it looks cute.
☐ One door closes, another opens.
☐ It's all part of the plan.
☐ Go ahead, cry it out.
☐ They spelled your name right.
☐ Jobs come, jobs go.
☐ People come, people go.
☐ This must be hard for you.
☐ Time to get on with your life.
☐ Everyone's a critic.
☐ It's for the best.
☐ Don't go there.
☐ It's their loss.
☐ You can focus on your career.
☐ You can focus on your kids.
☐ Didn't kill ya; made ya stronger.
☐ Ours is not to reason why.
☐ Don't take it home with you.
☐ Timing is everything.
☐ You'll eventually love it.
☐ Think positive.
☐ Think denial.

☐ Someday you'll understand.
☐ Single life is actually better.
☐ Always darkest before the dawn.
☐ Just clear the browser history.
☐ You're still young.
☐ He isn't worth it.
☐ She isn't worth it.
☐ Where there's a will . . .
☐ Chalk it up to experience.
☐ Cross that bridge later.
☐ One day at a time.
☐ You can always get it fixed.
☐ Don't sweat the small stuff.
☐ Not over 'til the fat lady sings.
☐ It's all nonsense anyway.
☐ You gotta believe in you.
☐ I believe in you.
☐ Anything is possible.
☐ You reacted with integrity.
☐ You can sell it online.
☐ Don't get mad, get even.
☐ No one can tell it's a knockoff.
☐ Just say no.
☐ Hang in there, baby.
☐ If it's not one thing, it's another.
☐ It'll build character.
☐ It was meant to be.
☐ It wasn't meant to be.
☐ If it's meant to be, it'll happen.
☐ Keep your chin up.
☐ You don't need their approval.
☐ For every hill there's a valley.
☐ I would've done the same.
☐ Life goes on.
☐ Absence makes love stronger.
☐ Can't beat 'em? Join 'em.
☐ Shake it off.
☐ No one heard it.
☐ Better late than never.
☐ Better safe than sorry.
☐ And so it goes.
☐ The first cut is the deepest.
☐ Love hurts.
☐ Love stinks.
☐ Love is overrated.
☐ Soon this'll be a distant memory.
☐ Keep on truckin'.
☐ Quit worrying.
☐ It's water under the bridge.
☐ Don't dwell on it.

☐ Ya gotta do what ya gotta do.
☐ When it rains, it pours.
☐ Every rose has a thorn.
☐ You gave it your best shot.
☐ There, there.
☐ It takes all kinds.
☐ They're just jealous.
☐ It'll come when you're ready.
☐ Nobody mentioned it.
☐ Try to keep it in perspective.
☐ Put on your big girl panties.
☐ Put on your big boy briefs.
☐ There's a lid for every pot.
☐ He's probably out of town.
☐ Her phone is probably dead.
☐ You're better off.
☐ It happens sometimes.
☐ They don't understand you.
☐ It was an honest mistake.
☐ Money can't buy love.
☐ Adversity forges character.
☐ You'll feel better after a bath.
☐ You'll feel better after a drink.
☐ It'll make great memoir material.
☐ Quit blaming yourself.
☐ There's no such thing as normal.
☐ You'll show them.
☐ This will forge your character.
☐ You're a superstar.
☐ Just explain what happened.
☐ Don't compare.
☐ All parents screw up.
☐ All kids screw up.
☐ At least you have your health.
☐ He'll grow out of it.
☐ She'll grow out of it.
☐ Shhh. Shhh. It's okay now.
☐ Pain is temporary.
☐ I agree with you.
☐ One day you'll know why.
☐ You march to your own beat.
☐ Ignore what others think.
☐ Buck up, buckwheat.
☐ Everyone sympathizes.
☐ You're overthinking this.
☐ Get back up on the horse.
☐ Just give it some time.
☐ It's not the end of the world.
☐ It gets better.
☐ Really, it is.

☐ **TOTALLY OKAY** ☐ **PRETTY OKAY** ☐ **OKAY-ISH**

SIGNATURE MONTH DAY YEAR

"OKAY? OKAY. OKAY!"

IT'S GONNA BE OKAY

☐ RIGHT NOW ☐ FAIRLY SOON ☐ EVENTUALLY

- ☐ It'll grow back.
- ☐ You'll get over it.
- ☐ You can do this.
- ☐ It wasn't that obvious.
- ☐ This too shall pass.
- ☐ You're too good for him.
- ☐ You're too good for her.
- ☐ I'll never tell.
- ☐ Don't blame yourself.
- ☐ There are other fish in the sea.
- ☐ Tattoo removal is easier now.
- ☐ You are not your job.
- ☐ Your mother will never know.
- ☐ Nothing therapy won't cure.
- ☐ Just take a mulligan.
- ☐ Moving home is no big deal.
- ☐ Don't "should" all over yourself.
- ☐ At least you know you're right.
- ☐ You did your best.
- ☐ Can't win 'em all.
- ☐ You couldn't have known.
- ☐ My cousin had that and was fine.
- ☐ Laughter is the best medicine.
- ☐ Have faith.
- ☐ Penicillin clears that up fast.
- ☐ He wasn't thinking.
- ☐ She wasn't thinking.
- ☐ If at first you don't succeed . . .
- ☐ It's about quality, not quantity.
- ☐ That's not old, it's vintage.
- ☐ You're not old, you're vintage.
- ☐ Things happen for a reason.
- ☐ It'll look better in the morning.
- ☐ You can blog about it.
- ☐ We'll look back later and laugh.
- ☐ No one will ever know.
- ☐ Here's a hug.
- ☐ They don't deserve you.
- ☐ Every cloud has a silver lining.
- ☐ It was totally his fault.
- ☐ It was totally her fault.
- ☐ A rising tide lifts all boats.
- ☐ There are specialists for that.
- ☐ Think of the big picture.
- ☐ Don't let it bother you so much.
- ☐ No one saw you trip.
- ☐ You'll get that promotion soon.
- ☐ It could've been much worse.
- ☐ Aim for the stars.
- ☐ You'll forget about it, I promise.
- ☐ All publicity is good publicity.
- ☐ You can always return it.
- ☐ That was so understandable.
- ☐ You look great.
- ☐ You look great for your age.
- ☐ That happens to everyone.
- ☐ You made your point.
- ☐ Who wants that responsibility?
- ☐ It's not more than you can handle.
- ☐ Time heals all wounds.
- ☐ Time wounds all heels.
- ☐ I'm sure you don't normally do that.
- ☐ Success or not, you are loved.
- ☐ It's a journey, not a destination.
- ☐ It was a long shot anyway.
- ☐ Lesson learned.
- ☐ It's not you, it's the economy.
- ☐ You can always sue.
- ☐ You're the bigger person.
- ☐ You still have your honor.
- ☐ You still have your hair.
- ☐ Heartbreak makes you wiser.
- ☐ People will see through that.
- ☐ You'll be the last one standing.
- ☐ Don't let it get you down.
- ☐ It's not forever.
- ☐ There are always people like that.
- ☐ Never fear, karma's a bitch.
- ☐ I think it looks cute.
- ☐ One door closes, another opens.
- ☐ It's all part of the plan.
- ☐ Go ahead, cry it out.
- ☐ They spelled your name right.
- ☐ Jobs come, jobs go.
- ☐ People come, people go.
- ☐ This must be hard for you.
- ☐ Time to get on with your life.
- ☐ Everyone's a critic.
- ☐ It's for the best.
- ☐ Don't go there.
- ☐ It's their loss.
- ☐ You can focus on your career.
- ☐ You can focus on your kids.
- ☐ Didn't kill ya; made ya stronger.
- ☐ Ours is not to reason why.
- ☐ Don't take it home with you.
- ☐ Timing is everything.
- ☐ You'll eventually love it.
- ☐ Think positive.
- ☐ Think denial.
- ☐ Someday you'll understand.
- ☐ Single life is actually better.
- ☐ Always darkest before the dawn.
- ☐ Just clear the browser history.
- ☐ You're still young.
- ☐ He isn't worth it.
- ☐ She isn't worth it.
- ☐ Where there's a will . . .
- ☐ Chalk it up to experience.
- ☐ Cross that bridge later.
- ☐ One day at a time.
- ☐ You can always get it fixed.
- ☐ Don't sweat the small stuff.
- ☐ Not over 'til the fat lady sings.
- ☐ It's all nonsense anyway.
- ☐ You gotta believe in you.
- ☐ I believe in you.
- ☐ Anything is possible.
- ☐ You reacted with integrity.
- ☐ You can sell it online.
- ☐ Don't get mad, get even.
- ☐ No one can tell it's a knockoff.
- ☐ Just say no.
- ☐ Hang in there, baby.
- ☐ If it's not one thing, it's another.
- ☐ It'll build character.
- ☐ It was meant to be.
- ☐ It wasn't meant to be.
- ☐ If it's meant to be, it'll happen.
- ☐ Keep your chin up.
- ☐ You don't need their approval.
- ☐ For every hill there's a valley.
- ☐ I would've done the same.
- ☐ Life goes on.
- ☐ Absence makes love stronger.
- ☐ Can't beat 'em? Join 'em.
- ☐ Shake it off.
- ☐ No one heard it.
- ☐ Better late than never.
- ☐ Better safe than sorry.
- ☐ And so it goes.
- ☐ The first cut is the deepest.
- ☐ Love hurts.
- ☐ Love stinks.
- ☐ Love is overrated.
- ☐ Soon this'll be a distant memory.
- ☐ Keep on truckin'.
- ☐ Quit worrying.
- ☐ It's water under the bridge.
- ☐ Don't dwell on it.
- ☐ Ya gotta do what ya gotta do.
- ☐ When it rains, it pours.
- ☐ Every rose has a thorn.
- ☐ You gave it your best shot.
- ☐ There, there.
- ☐ It takes all kinds.
- ☐ They're just jealous.
- ☐ It'll come when you're ready.
- ☐ Nobody mentioned it.
- ☐ Try to keep it in perspective.
- ☐ Put on your big girl panties.
- ☐ Put on your big boy briefs.
- ☐ There's a lid for every pot.
- ☐ He's probably out of town.
- ☐ Her phone is probably dead.
- ☐ You're better off.
- ☐ It happens sometimes.
- ☐ They don't understand you.
- ☐ It was an honest mistake.
- ☐ Money can't buy love.
- ☐ Adversity forges character.
- ☐ You'll feel better after a bath.
- ☐ You'll feel better after a drink.
- ☐ It'll make great memoir material.
- ☐ Quit blaming yourself.
- ☐ There's no such thing as normal.
- ☐ You'll show them.
- ☐ This will forge your character.
- ☐ You're a superstar.
- ☐ Just explain what happened.
- ☐ Don't compare.
- ☐ All parents screw up.
- ☐ All kids screw up.
- ☐ At least you have your health.
- ☐ He'll grow out of it.
- ☐ She'll grow out of it.
- ☐ Shhh. Shhh. It's okay now.
- ☐ Pain is temporary.
- ☐ I agree with you.
- ☐ One day you'll know why.
- ☐ You march to your own beat.
- ☐ Ignore what others think.
- ☐ Buck up, buckwheat.
- ☐ Everyone sympathizes.
- ☐ You're overthinking this.
- ☐ Get back up on the horse.
- ☐ Just give it some time.
- ☐ It's not the end of the world.
- ☐ It gets better.
- ☐ Really, it is.

☐ TOTALLY OKAY ☐ PRETTY OKAY ☐ OKAY-ISH

SIGNATURE

MONTH : DAY : YEAR

"OKAY? OKAY. OKAY!"

IT'S GONNA BE OKAY

☐ **RIGHT NOW** ☐ **FAIRLY SOON** ☐ **EVENTUALLY**

☐ It'll grow back.
☐ You'll get over it.
☐ You can do this.
☐ It wasn't that obvious.
☐ This too shall pass.
☐ You're too good for him.
☐ You're too good for her.
☐ I'll never tell.
☐ Don't blame yourself.
☐ There are other fish in the sea.
☐ Tattoo removal is easier now.
☐ You are not your job.
☐ Your mother will never know.
☐ Nothing therapy won't cure.
☐ Just take a mulligan.
☐ Moving home is no big deal.
☐ Don't "should" all over yourself.
☐ At least you know you're right.
☐ You did your best.
☐ Can't win 'em all.
☐ You couldn't have known.
☐ My cousin had that and was fine.
☐ Laughter is the best medicine.
☐ Have faith.
☐ Penicillin clears that up fast.
☐ He wasn't thinking.
☐ She wasn't thinking.
☐ If at first you don't succeed . . .
☐ It's about quality, not quantity.
☐ That's not old, it's vintage.
☐ You're not old, you're vintage.
☐ Things happen for a reason.
☐ It'll look better in the morning.
☐ You can blog about it.
☐ We'll look back later and laugh.
☐ No one will ever know.
☐ Here's a hug.
☐ They don't deserve you.
☐ Every cloud has a silver lining.
☐ It was totally his fault.
☐ It was totally her fault.
☐ A rising tide lifts all boats.
☐ There are specialists for that.
☐ Think of the big picture.
☐ Don't let it bother you so much.
☐ No one saw you trip.
☐ You'll get that promotion soon.
☐ It could've been much worse.
☐ Aim for the stars.
☐ You'll forget about it, I promise.

☐ All publicity is good publicity.
☐ You can always return it.
☐ That was so understandable.
☐ You look great.
☐ You look great for your age.
☐ That happens to everyone.
☐ You made your point.
☐ Who wants that responsibility?
☐ It's not more than you can handle.
☐ Time heals all wounds.
☐ Time wounds all heels.
☐ I'm sure you don't normally do that.
☐ Success or not, you are loved.
☐ It's a journey, not a destination.
☐ It was a long shot anyway.
☐ Lesson learned.
☐ It's not you, it's the economy.
☐ You can always sue.
☐ You're the bigger person.
☐ You still have your honor.
☐ You still have your hair.
☐ Heartbreak makes you wiser.
☐ People will see through that.
☐ You'll be the last one standing.
☐ Don't let it get you down.
☐ It's not forever.
☐ There are always people like that.
☐ Never fear, karma's a bitch.
☐ I think it looks cute.
☐ One door closes, another opens.
☐ It's all part of the plan.
☐ Go ahead, cry it out.
☐ They spelled your name right.
☐ Jobs come, jobs go.
☐ People come, people go.
☐ This must be hard for you.
☐ Time to get on with your life.
☐ Everyone's a critic.
☐ It's for the best.
☐ Don't go there.
☐ It's their loss.
☐ You can focus on your career.
☐ You can focus on your kids.
☐ Didn't kill ya; made ya stronger.
☐ Ours is not to reason why.
☐ Don't take it home with you.
☐ Timing is everything.
☐ You'll eventually love it.
☐ Think positive.
☐ Think denial.

☐ Someday you'll understand.
☐ Single life is actually better.
☐ Always darkest before the dawn.
☐ Just clear the browser history.
☐ You're still young.
☐ He isn't worth it.
☐ She isn't worth it.
☐ Where there's a will . . .
☐ Chalk it up to experience.
☐ Cross that bridge later.
☐ One day at a time.
☐ You can always get it fixed.
☐ Don't sweat the small stuff.
☐ Not over 'til the fat lady sings.
☐ It's all nonsense anyway.
☐ You gotta believe in you.
☐ I believe in you.
☐ Anything is possible.
☐ You reacted with integrity.
☐ You can sell it online.
☐ Don't get mad, get even.
☐ No one can tell it's a knockoff.
☐ Just say no.
☐ Hang in there, baby.
☐ If it's not one thing, it's another.
☐ It'll build character.
☐ It was meant to be.
☐ It wasn't meant to be.
☐ If it's meant to be, it'll happen.
☐ Keep your chin up.
☐ You don't need their approval.
☐ For every hill there's a valley.
☐ I would've done the same.
☐ Life goes on.
☐ Absence makes love stronger.
☐ Can't beat 'em? Join 'em.
☐ Shake it off.
☐ No one heard it.
☐ Better late than never.
☐ Better safe than sorry.
☐ And so it goes.
☐ The first cut is the deepest.
☐ Love hurts.
☐ Love stinks.
☐ Love is overrated.
☐ Soon this'll be a distant memory.
☐ Keep on truckin'.
☐ Quit worrying.
☐ It's water under the bridge.
☐ Don't dwell on it.

☐ Ya gotta do what ya gotta do.
☐ When it rains, it pours.
☐ Every rose has a thorn.
☐ You gave it your best shot.
☐ There, there.
☐ It takes all kinds.
☐ They're just jealous.
☐ It'll come when you're ready.
☐ Nobody mentioned it.
☐ Try to keep it in perspective.
☐ Put on your big girl panties.
☐ Put on your big boy briefs.
☐ There's a lid for every pot.
☐ He's probably out of town.
☐ Her phone is probably dead.
☐ You're better off.
☐ It happens sometimes.
☐ They don't understand you.
☐ It was an honest mistake.
☐ Money can't buy love.
☐ Adversity forges character.
☐ You'll feel better after a bath.
☐ You'll feel better after a drink.
☐ It'll make great memoir material.
☐ Quit blaming yourself.
☐ There's no such thing as normal.
☐ You'll show them.
☐ This will forge your character.
☐ You're a superstar.
☐ Just explain what happened.
☐ Don't compare.
☐ All parents screw up.
☐ All kids screw up.
☐ At least you have your health.
☐ He'll grow out of it.
☐ She'll grow out of it.
☐ Shhh. Shhh. It's okay now.
☐ Pain is temporary.
☐ I agree with you.
☐ One day you'll know why.
☐ You march to your own beat.
☐ Ignore what others think.
☐ Buck up, buckwheat.
☐ Everyone sympathizes.
☐ You're overthinking this.
☐ Get back up on the horse.
☐ Just give it some time.
☐ It's not the end of the world.
☐ It gets better.
☐ Really, it is.

☐ **TOTALLY OKAY** ☐ **PRETTY OKAY** ☐ **OKAY-ISH**

SIGNATURE

MONTH DAY YEAR

"OKAY? OKAY. OKAY!"

IT'S GONNA BE OKAY

☐ RIGHT NOW ☐ FAIRLY SOON ☐ EVENTUALLY

☐ It'll grow back.
☐ You'll get over it.
☐ You can do this.
☐ It wasn't that obvious.
☐ This too shall pass.
☐ You're too good for him.
☐ You're too good for her.
☐ I'll never tell.
☐ Don't blame yourself.
☐ There are other fish in the sea.
☐ Tattoo removal is easier now.
☐ You are not your job.
☐ Your mother will never know.
☐ Nothing therapy won't cure.
☐ Just take a mulligan.
☐ Moving home is no big deal.
☐ Don't "should" all over yourself.
☐ At least you know you're right.
☐ You did your best.
☐ Can't win 'em all.
☐ You couldn't have known.
☐ My cousin had that and was fine.
☐ Laughter is the best medicine.
☐ Have faith.
☐ Penicillin clears that up fast.
☐ He wasn't thinking.
☐ She wasn't thinking.
☐ If at first you don't succeed . . .
☐ It's about quality, not quantity.
☐ That's not old, it's vintage.
☐ You're not old, you're vintage.
☐ Things happen for a reason.
☐ It'll look better in the morning.
☐ You can blog about it.
☐ We'll look back later and laugh.
☐ No one will ever know.
☐ Here's a hug.
☐ They don't deserve you.
☐ Every cloud has a silver lining.
☐ It was totally his fault.
☐ It was totally her fault.
☐ A rising tide lifts all boats.
☐ There are specialists for that.
☐ Think of the big picture.
☐ Don't let it bother you so much.
☐ No one saw you trip.
☐ You'll get that promotion soon.
☐ It could've been much worse.
☐ Aim for the stars.
☐ You'll forget about it, I promise.

☐ All publicity is good publicity.
☐ You can always return it.
☐ That was so understandable.
☐ You look great.
☐ You look great for your age.
☐ That happens to everyone.
☐ You made your point.
☐ Who wants that responsibility?
☐ It's not more than you can handle.
☐ Time heals all wounds.
☐ Time wounds all heels.
☐ I'm sure you don't normally do that.
☐ Success or not, you are loved.
☐ It's a journey, not a destination.
☐ It was a long shot anyway.
☐ Lesson learned.
☐ It's not you, it's the economy.
☐ You can always sue.
☐ You're the bigger person.
☐ You still have your honor.
☐ You still have your hair.
☐ Heartbreak makes you wiser.
☐ People will see through that.
☐ You'll be the last one standing.
☐ Don't let it get you down.
☐ It's not forever.
☐ There are always people like that.
☐ Never fear, karma's a bitch.
☐ I think it looks cute.
☐ One door closes, another opens.
☐ It's all part of the plan.
☐ Go ahead, cry it out.
☐ They spelled your name right.
☐ Jobs come, jobs go.
☐ People come, people go.
☐ This must be hard for you.
☐ Time to get on with your life.
☐ Everyone's a critic.
☐ It's for the best.
☐ Don't go there.
☐ It's their loss.
☐ You can focus on your career.
☐ You can focus on your kids.
☐ Didn't kill ya; made ya stronger.
☐ Ours is not to reason why.
☐ Don't take it home with you.
☐ Timing is everything.
☐ You'll eventually love it.
☐ Think positive.
☐ Think denial.

☐ Someday you'll understand.
☐ Single life is actually better.
☐ Always darkest before the dawn.
☐ Just clear the browser history.
☐ You're still young.
☐ He isn't worth it.
☐ She isn't worth it.
☐ Where there's a will . . .
☐ Chalk it up to experience.
☐ Cross that bridge later.
☐ One day at a time.
☐ You can always get it fixed.
☐ Don't sweat the small stuff.
☐ Not over 'til the fat lady sings.
☐ It's all nonsense anyway.
☐ You gotta believe in you.
☐ I believe in you.
☐ Anything is possible.
☐ You reacted with integrity.
☐ You can sell it online.
☐ Don't get mad, get even.
☐ No one can tell it's a knockoff.
☐ Just say no.
☐ Hang in there, baby.
☐ If it's not one thing, it's another.
☐ It'll build character.
☐ It was meant to be.
☐ It wasn't meant to be.
☐ If it's meant to be, it'll happen.
☐ Keep your chin up.
☐ You don't need their approval.
☐ For every hill there's a valley.
☐ I would've done the same.
☐ Life goes on.
☐ Absence makes love stronger.
☐ Can't beat 'em? Join 'em.
☐ Shake it off.
☐ No one heard it.
☐ Better late than never.
☐ Better safe than sorry.
☐ And so it goes.
☐ The first cut is the deepest.
☐ Love hurts.
☐ Love stinks.
☐ Love is overrated.
☐ Soon this'll be a distant memory.
☐ Keep on truckin'.
☐ Quit worrying.
☐ It's water under the bridge.
☐ Don't dwell on it.

☐ Ya gotta do what ya gotta do.
☐ When it rains, it pours.
☐ Every rose has a thorn.
☐ You gave it your best shot.
☐ There, there.
☐ It takes all kinds.
☐ They're just jealous.
☐ It'll come when you're ready.
☐ Nobody mentioned it.
☐ Try to keep it in perspective.
☐ Put on your big girl panties.
☐ Put on your big boy briefs.
☐ There's a lid for every pot.
☐ He's probably out of town.
☐ Her phone is probably dead.
☐ You're better off.
☐ It happens sometimes.
☐ They don't understand you.
☐ It was an honest mistake.
☐ Money can't buy love.
☐ Adversity forges character.
☐ You'll feel better after a bath.
☐ You'll feel better after a drink.
☐ It'll make great memoir material.
☐ Quit blaming yourself.
☐ There's no such thing as normal.
☐ You'll show them.
☐ This will forge your character.
☐ You're a superstar.
☐ Just explain what happened.
☐ Don't compare.
☐ All parents screw up.
☐ All kids screw up.
☐ At least you have your health.
☐ He'll grow out of it.
☐ She'll grow out of it.
☐ Shhh. Shhh. It's okay now.
☐ Pain is temporary.
☐ I agree with you.
☐ One day you'll know why.
☐ You march to your own beat.
☐ Ignore what others think.
☐ Buck up, buckwheat.
☐ Everyone sympathizes.
☐ You're overthinking this.
☐ Get back up on the horse.
☐ Just give it some time.
☐ It's not the end of the world.
☐ It gets better.
☐ Really, it is.

☐ TOTALLY OKAY ☐ PRETTY OKAY ☐ OKAY-ISH

SIGNATURE MONTH DAY YEAR

"OKAY? OKAY. OKAY!"

IT'S GONNA BE OKAY

☐ **RIGHT NOW** ☐ **FAIRLY SOON** ☐ **EVENTUALLY**

- ☐ It'll grow back.
- ☐ You'll get over it.
- ☐ You can do this.
- ☐ It wasn't that obvious.
- ☐ This too shall pass.
- ☐ You're too good for him.
- ☐ You're too good for her.
- ☐ I'll never tell.
- ☐ Don't blame yourself.
- ☐ There are other fish in the sea.
- ☐ Tattoo removal is easier now.
- ☐ You are not your job.
- ☐ Your mother will never know.
- ☐ Nothing therapy won't cure.
- ☐ Just take a mulligan.
- ☐ Moving home is no big deal.
- ☐ Don't "should" all over yourself.
- ☐ At least you know you're right.
- ☐ You did your best.
- ☐ Can't win 'em all.
- ☐ You couldn't have known.
- ☐ My cousin had that and was fine.
- ☐ Laughter is the best medicine.
- ☐ Have faith.
- ☐ Penicillin clears that up fast.
- ☐ He wasn't thinking.
- ☐ She wasn't thinking.
- ☐ If at first you don't succeed . . .
- ☐ It's about quality, not quantity.
- ☐ That's not old, it's vintage.
- ☐ You're not old, you're vintage.
- ☐ Things happen for a reason.
- ☐ It'll look better in the morning.
- ☐ You can blog about it.
- ☐ We'll look back later and laugh.
- ☐ No one will ever know.
- ☐ Here's a hug.
- ☐ They don't deserve you.
- ☐ Every cloud has a silver lining.
- ☐ It was totally his fault.
- ☐ It was totally her fault.
- ☐ A rising tide lifts all boats.
- ☐ There are specialists for that.
- ☐ Think of the big picture.
- ☐ Don't let it bother you so much.
- ☐ No one saw you trip.
- ☐ You'll get that promotion soon.
- ☐ It could've been much worse.
- ☐ Aim for the stars.
- ☐ You'll forget about it, I promise.

- ☐ All publicity is good publicity.
- ☐ You can always return it.
- ☐ That was so understandable.
- ☐ You look great.
- ☐ You look great for your age.
- ☐ That happens to everyone.
- ☐ You made your point.
- ☐ Who wants that responsibility?
- ☐ It's not more than you can handle.
- ☐ Time heals all wounds.
- ☐ Time wounds all heels.
- ☐ I'm sure you don't normally do that.
- ☐ Success or not, you are loved.
- ☐ It's a journey, not a destination.
- ☐ It was a long shot anyway.
- ☐ Lesson learned.
- ☐ It's not you, it's the economy.
- ☐ You can always sue.
- ☐ You're the bigger person.
- ☐ You still have your honor.
- ☐ You still have your hair.
- ☐ Heartbreak makes you wiser.
- ☐ People will see through that.
- ☐ You'll be the last one standing.
- ☐ Don't let it get you down.
- ☐ It's not forever.
- ☐ There are always people like that.
- ☐ Never fear, karma's a bitch.
- ☐ I think it looks cute.
- ☐ One door closes, another opens.
- ☐ It's all part of the plan.
- ☐ Go ahead, cry it out.
- ☐ They spelled your name right.
- ☐ Jobs come, jobs go.
- ☐ People come, people go.
- ☐ This must be hard for you.
- ☐ Time to get on with your life.
- ☐ Everyone's a critic.
- ☐ It's for the best.
- ☐ Don't go there.
- ☐ It's their loss.
- ☐ You can focus on your career.
- ☐ You can focus on your kids.
- ☐ Didn't kill ya; made ya stronger.
- ☐ Ours is not to reason why.
- ☐ Don't take it home with you.
- ☐ Timing is everything.
- ☐ You'll eventually love it.
- ☐ Think positive.
- ☐ Think denial.

- ☐ Someday you'll understand.
- ☐ Single life is actually better.
- ☐ Always darkest before the dawn.
- ☐ Just clear the browser history.
- ☐ You're still young.
- ☐ He isn't worth it.
- ☐ She isn't worth it.
- ☐ Where there's a will . . .
- ☐ Chalk it up to experience.
- ☐ Cross that bridge later.
- ☐ One day at a time.
- ☐ You can always get it fixed.
- ☐ Don't sweat the small stuff.
- ☐ Not over 'til the fat lady sings.
- ☐ It's all nonsense anyway.
- ☐ You gotta believe in you.
- ☐ I believe in you.
- ☐ Anything is possible.
- ☐ You reacted with integrity.
- ☐ You can sell it online.
- ☐ Don't get mad, get even.
- ☐ No one can tell it's a knockoff.
- ☐ Just say no.
- ☐ Hang in there, baby.
- ☐ If it's not one thing, it's another.
- ☐ It'll build character.
- ☐ It was meant to be.
- ☐ It wasn't meant to be.
- ☐ If it's meant to be, it'll happen.
- ☐ Keep your chin up.
- ☐ You don't need their approval.
- ☐ For every hill there's a valley.
- ☐ I would've done the same.
- ☐ Life goes on.
- ☐ Absence makes love stronger.
- ☐ Can't beat 'em? Join 'em.
- ☐ Shake it off.
- ☐ No one heard it.
- ☐ Better late than never.
- ☐ Better safe than sorry.
- ☐ And so it goes.
- ☐ The first cut is the deepest.
- ☐ Love hurts.
- ☐ Love stinks.
- ☐ Love is overrated.
- ☐ Soon this'll be a distant memory.
- ☐ Keep on truckin'.
- ☐ Quit worrying.
- ☐ It's water under the bridge.
- ☐ Don't dwell on it.

- ☐ Ya gotta do what ya gotta do.
- ☐ When it rains, it pours.
- ☐ Every rose has a thorn.
- ☐ You gave it your best shot.
- ☐ There, there.
- ☐ It takes all kinds.
- ☐ They're just jealous.
- ☐ It'll come when you're ready.
- ☐ Nobody mentioned it.
- ☐ Try to keep it in perspective.
- ☐ Put on your big girl panties.
- ☐ Put on your big boy briefs.
- ☐ There's a lid for every pot.
- ☐ He's probably out of town.
- ☐ Her phone is probably dead.
- ☐ You're better off.
- ☐ It happens sometimes.
- ☐ They don't understand you.
- ☐ It was an honest mistake.
- ☐ Money can't buy love.
- ☐ Adversity forges character.
- ☐ You'll feel better after a bath.
- ☐ You'll feel better after a drink.
- ☐ It'll make great memoir material.
- ☐ Quit blaming yourself.
- ☐ There's no such thing as normal.
- ☐ You'll show them.
- ☐ This will forge your character.
- ☐ You're a superstar.
- ☐ Just explain what happened.
- ☐ Don't compare.
- ☐ All parents screw up.
- ☐ All kids screw up.
- ☐ At least you have your health.
- ☐ He'll grow out of it.
- ☐ She'll grow out of it.
- ☐ Shhh. Shhh. It's okay now.
- ☐ Pain is temporary.
- ☐ I agree with you.
- ☐ One day you'll know why.
- ☐ You march to your own beat.
- ☐ Ignore what others think.
- ☐ Buck up, buckwheat.
- ☐ Everyone sympathizes.
- ☐ You're overthinking this.
- ☐ Get back up on the horse.
- ☐ Just give it some time.
- ☐ It's not the end of the world.
- ☐ It gets better.
- ☐ Really, it is.

☐ **TOTALLY OKAY** ☐ **PRETTY OKAY** ☐ **OKAY-ISH**

SIGNATURE	MONTH	DAY	YEAR

"OKAY? OKAY. OKAY!"

IT'S GONNA BE OKAY

☐ **RIGHT NOW** ☐ **FAIRLY SOON** ☐ **EVENTUALLY**

☐ It'll grow back.
☐ You'll get over it.
☐ You can do this.
☐ It wasn't that obvious.
☐ This too shall pass.
☐ You're too good for him.
☐ You're too good for her.
☐ I'll never tell.
☐ Don't blame yourself.
☐ There are other fish in the sea.
☐ Tattoo removal is easier now.
☐ You are not your job.
☐ Your mother will never know.
☐ Nothing therapy won't cure.
☐ Just take a mulligan.
☐ Moving home is no big deal.
☐ Don't "should" all over yourself.
☐ At least you know you're right.
☐ You did your best.
☐ Can't win 'em all.
☐ You couldn't have known.
☐ My cousin had that and was fine.
☐ Laughter is the best medicine.
☐ Have faith.
☐ Penicillin clears that up fast.
☐ He wasn't thinking.
☐ She wasn't thinking.
☐ If at first you don't succeed . . .
☐ It's about quality, not quantity.
☐ That's not old, it's vintage.
☐ You're not old, you're vintage.
☐ Things happen for a reason.
☐ It'll look better in the morning.
☐ You can blog about it.
☐ We'll look back later and laugh.
☐ No one will ever know.
☐ Here's a hug.
☐ They don't deserve you.
☐ Every cloud has a silver lining.
☐ It was totally his fault.
☐ It was totally her fault.
☐ A rising tide lifts all boats.
☐ There are specialists for that.
☐ Think of the big picture.
☐ Don't let it bother you so much.
☐ No one saw you trip.
☐ You'll get that promotion soon.
☐ It could've been much worse.
☐ Aim for the stars.
☐ You'll forget about it, I promise.

☐ All publicity is good publicity.
☐ You can always return it.
☐ That was so understandable.
☐ You look great.
☐ You look great for your age.
☐ That happens to everyone.
☐ You made your point.
☐ Who wants that responsibility?
☐ It's not more than you can handle.
☐ Time heals all wounds.
☐ Time wounds all heels.
☐ I'm sure you don't normally do that.
☐ Success or not, you are loved.
☐ It's a journey, not a destination.
☐ It was a long shot anyway.
☐ Lesson learned.
☐ It's not you, it's the economy.
☐ You can always sue.
☐ You're the bigger person.
☐ You still have your honor.
☐ You still have your hair.
☐ Heartbreak makes you wiser.
☐ People will see through that.
☐ You'll be the last one standing.
☐ Don't let it get you down.
☐ It's not forever.
☐ There are always people like that.
☐ Never fear, karma's a bitch.
☐ I think it looks cute.
☐ One door closes, another opens.
☐ It's all part of the plan.
☐ Go ahead, cry it out.
☐ They spelled your name right.
☐ Jobs come, jobs go.
☐ People come, people go.
☐ This must be hard for you.
☐ Time to get on with your life.
☐ Everyone's a critic.
☐ It's for the best.
☐ Don't go there.
☐ It's their loss.
☐ You can focus on your career.
☐ You can focus on your kids.
☐ Didn't kill ya; made ya stronger.
☐ Ours is not to reason why.
☐ Don't take it home with you.
☐ Timing is everything.
☐ You'll eventually love it.
☐ Think positive.
☐ Think denial.

☐ Someday you'll understand.
☐ Single life is actually better.
☐ Always darkest before the dawn.
☐ Just clear the browser history.
☐ You're still young.
☐ He isn't worth it.
☐ She isn't worth it.
☐ Where there's a will . . .
☐ Chalk it up to experience.
☐ Cross that bridge later.
☐ One day at a time.
☐ You can always get it fixed.
☐ Don't sweat the small stuff.
☐ Not over 'til the fat lady sings.
☐ It's all nonsense anyway.
☐ You gotta believe in you.
☐ I believe in you.
☐ Anything is possible.
☐ You reacted with integrity.
☐ You can sell it online.
☐ Don't get mad, get even.
☐ No one can tell it's a knockoff.
☐ Just say no.
☐ Hang in there, baby.
☐ If it's not one thing, it's another.
☐ It'll build character.
☐ It was meant to be.
☐ It wasn't meant to be.
☐ If it's meant to be, it'll happen.
☐ Keep your chin up.
☐ You don't need their approval.
☐ For every hill there's a valley.
☐ I would've done the same.
☐ Life goes on.
☐ Absence makes love stronger.
☐ Can't beat 'em? Join 'em.
☐ Shake it off.
☐ No one heard it.
☐ Better late than never.
☐ Better safe than sorry.
☐ And so it goes.
☐ The first cut is the deepest.
☐ Love hurts.
☐ Love stinks.
☐ Love is overrated.
☐ Soon this'll be a distant memory.
☐ Keep on truckin'.
☐ Quit worrying.
☐ It's water under the bridge.
☐ Don't dwell on it.

☐ Ya gotta do what ya gotta do.
☐ When it rains, it pours.
☐ Every rose has a thorn.
☐ You gave it your best shot.
☐ There, there.
☐ It takes all kinds.
☐ They're just jealous.
☐ It'll come when you're ready.
☐ Nobody mentioned it.
☐ Try to keep it in perspective.
☐ Put on your big girl panties.
☐ Put on your big boy briefs.
☐ There's a lid for every pot.
☐ He's probably out of town.
☐ Her phone is probably dead.
☐ You're better off.
☐ It happens sometimes.
☐ They don't understand you.
☐ It was an honest mistake.
☐ Money can't buy love.
☐ Adversity forges character.
☐ You'll feel better after a bath.
☐ You'll feel better after a drink.
☐ It'll make great memoir material.
☐ Quit blaming yourself.
☐ There's no such thing as normal.
☐ You'll show them.
☐ This will forge your character.
☐ You're a superstar.
☐ Just explain what happened.
☐ Don't compare.
☐ All parents screw up.
☐ All kids screw up.
☐ At least you have your health.
☐ He'll grow out of it.
☐ She'll grow out of it.
☐ Shhh. Shhh. It's okay now.
☐ Pain is temporary.
☐ I agree with you.
☐ One day you'll know why.
☐ You march to your own beat.
☐ Ignore what others think.
☐ Buck up, buckwheat.
☐ Everyone sympathizes.
☐ You're overthinking this.
☐ Get back up on the horse.
☐ Just give it some time.
☐ It's not the end of the world.
☐ It gets better.
☐ Really, it is.

☐ **TOTALLY OKAY** ☐ **PRETTY OKAY** ☐ **OKAY-ISH**

SIGNATURE

MONTH DAY YEAR

"OKAY? OKAY. OKAY!"

IT'S GONNA BE OKAY

☐ RIGHT NOW ☐ FAIRLY SOON ☐ EVENTUALLY

- ☐ It'll grow back.
- ☐ You'll get over it.
- ☐ You can do this.
- ☐ It wasn't that obvious.
- ☐ This too shall pass.
- ☐ You're too good for him.
- ☐ You're too good for her.
- ☐ I'll never tell.
- ☐ Don't blame yourself.
- ☐ There are other fish in the sea.
- ☐ Tattoo removal is easier now.
- ☐ You are not your job.
- ☐ Your mother will never know.
- ☐ Nothing therapy won't cure.
- ☐ Just take a mulligan.
- ☐ Moving home is no big deal.
- ☐ Don't "should" all over yourself.
- ☐ At least you know you're right.
- ☐ You did your best.
- ☐ Can't win 'em all.
- ☐ You couldn't have known.
- ☐ My cousin had that and was fine.
- ☐ Laughter is the best medicine.
- ☐ Have faith.
- ☐ Penicillin clears that up fast.
- ☐ He wasn't thinking.
- ☐ She wasn't thinking.
- ☐ If at first you don't succeed . . .
- ☐ It's about quality, not quantity.
- ☐ That's not old, it's vintage.
- ☐ You're not old, you're vintage.
- ☐ Things happen for a reason.
- ☐ It'll look better in the morning.
- ☐ You can blog about it.
- ☐ We'll look back later and laugh.
- ☐ No one will ever know.
- ☐ Here's a hug.
- ☐ They don't deserve you.
- ☐ Every cloud has a silver lining.
- ☐ It was totally his fault.
- ☐ It was totally her fault.
- ☐ A rising tide lifts all boats.
- ☐ There are specialists for that.
- ☐ Think of the big picture.
- ☐ Don't let it bother you so much.
- ☐ No one saw you trip.
- ☐ You'll get that promotion soon.
- ☐ It could've been much worse.
- ☐ Aim for the stars.
- ☐ You'll forget about it, I promise.
- ☐ All publicity is good publicity.
- ☐ You can always return it.
- ☐ That was so understandable.
- ☐ You look great.
- ☐ You look great for your age.
- ☐ That happens to everyone.
- ☐ You made your point.
- ☐ Who wants that responsibility?
- ☐ It's not more than you can handle.
- ☐ Time heals all wounds.
- ☐ Time wounds all heels.
- ☐ I'm sure you don't normally do that.
- ☐ Success or not, you are loved.
- ☐ It's a journey, not a destination.
- ☐ It was a long shot anyway.
- ☐ Lesson learned.
- ☐ It's not you, it's the economy.
- ☐ You can always sue.
- ☐ You're the bigger person.
- ☐ You still have your honor.
- ☐ You still have your hair.
- ☐ Heartbreak makes you wiser.
- ☐ People will see through that.
- ☐ You'll be the last one standing.
- ☐ Don't let it get you down.
- ☐ It's not forever.
- ☐ There are always people like that.
- ☐ Never fear, karma's a bitch.
- ☐ I think it looks cute.
- ☐ One door closes, another opens.
- ☐ It's all part of the plan.
- ☐ Go ahead, cry it out.
- ☐ They spelled your name right.
- ☐ Jobs come, jobs go.
- ☐ People come, people go.
- ☐ This must be hard for you.
- ☐ Time to get on with your life.
- ☐ Everyone's a critic.
- ☐ It's for the best.
- ☐ Don't go there.
- ☐ It's their loss.
- ☐ You can focus on your career.
- ☐ You can focus on your kids.
- ☐ Didn't kill ya; made ya stronger.
- ☐ Ours is not to reason why.
- ☐ Don't take it home with you.
- ☐ Timing is everything.
- ☐ You'll eventually love it.
- ☐ Think positive.
- ☐ Think denial.
- ☐ Someday you'll understand.
- ☐ Single life is actually better.
- ☐ Always darkest before the dawn.
- ☐ Just clear the browser history.
- ☐ You're still young.
- ☐ He isn't worth it.
- ☐ She isn't worth it.
- ☐ Where there's a will . . .
- ☐ Chalk it up to experience.
- ☐ Cross that bridge later.
- ☐ One day at a time.
- ☐ You can always get it fixed.
- ☐ Don't sweat the small stuff.
- ☐ Not over 'til the fat lady sings.
- ☐ It's all nonsense anyway.
- ☐ You gotta believe in you.
- ☐ I believe in you.
- ☐ Anything is possible.
- ☐ You reacted with integrity.
- ☐ You can sell it online.
- ☐ Don't get mad, get even.
- ☐ No one can tell it's a knockoff.
- ☐ Just say no.
- ☐ Hang in there, baby.
- ☐ If it's not one thing, it's another.
- ☐ It'll build character.
- ☐ It was meant to be.
- ☐ It wasn't meant to be.
- ☐ If it's meant to be, it'll happen.
- ☐ Keep your chin up.
- ☐ You don't need their approval.
- ☐ For every hill there's a valley.
- ☐ I would've done the same.
- ☐ Life goes on.
- ☐ Absence makes love stronger.
- ☐ Can't beat 'em? Join 'em.
- ☐ Shake it off.
- ☐ No one heard it.
- ☐ Better late than never.
- ☐ Better safe than sorry.
- ☐ And so it goes.
- ☐ The first cut is the deepest.
- ☐ Love hurts.
- ☐ Love stinks.
- ☐ Love is overrated.
- ☐ Soon this'll be a distant memory.
- ☐ Keep on truckin'.
- ☐ Quit worrying.
- ☐ It's water under the bridge.
- ☐ Don't dwell on it.
- ☐ Ya gotta do what ya gotta do.
- ☐ When it rains, it pours.
- ☐ Every rose has a thorn.
- ☐ You gave it your best shot.
- ☐ There, there.
- ☐ It takes all kinds.
- ☐ They're just jealous.
- ☐ It'll come when you're ready.
- ☐ Nobody mentioned it.
- ☐ Try to keep it in perspective.
- ☐ Put on your big girl panties.
- ☐ Put on your big boy briefs.
- ☐ There's a lid for every pot.
- ☐ He's probably out of town.
- ☐ Her phone is probably dead.
- ☐ You're better off.
- ☐ It happens sometimes.
- ☐ They don't understand you.
- ☐ It was an honest mistake.
- ☐ Money can't buy love.
- ☐ Adversity forges character.
- ☐ You'll feel better after a bath.
- ☐ You'll feel better after a drink.
- ☐ It'll make great memoir material.
- ☐ Quit blaming yourself.
- ☐ There's no such thing as normal.
- ☐ You'll show them.
- ☐ This will forge your character.
- ☐ You're a superstar.
- ☐ Just explain what happened.
- ☐ Don't compare.
- ☐ All parents screw up.
- ☐ All kids screw up.
- ☐ At least you have your health.
- ☐ He'll grow out of it.
- ☐ She'll grow out of it.
- ☐ Shhh. Shhh. It's okay now.
- ☐ Pain is temporary.
- ☐ I agree with you.
- ☐ One day you'll know why.
- ☐ You march to your own beat.
- ☐ Ignore what others think.
- ☐ Buck up, buckwheat.
- ☐ Everyone sympathizes.
- ☐ You're overthinking this.
- ☐ Get back up on the horse.
- ☐ Just give it some time.
- ☐ It's not the end of the world.
- ☐ It gets better.
- ☐ Really, it is.

☐ TOTALLY OKAY ☐ PRETTY OKAY ☐ OKAY-ISH

SIGNATURE

MONTH DAY YEAR

"OKAY? OKAY. OKAY!"

IT'S GONNA BE OKAY

☐ **RIGHT NOW** ☐ **FAIRLY SOON** ☐ **EVENTUALLY**

☐ It'll grow back.
☐ You'll get over it.
☐ You can do this.
☐ It wasn't that obvious.
☐ This too shall pass.
☐ You're too good for him.
☐ You're too good for her.
☐ I'll never tell.
☐ Don't blame yourself.
☐ There are other fish in the sea.
☐ Tattoo removal is easier now.
☐ You are not your job.
☐ Your mother will never know.
☐ Nothing therapy won't cure.
☐ Just take a mulligan.
☐ Moving home is no big deal.
☐ Don't "should" all over yourself.
☐ At least you know you're right.
☐ You did your best.
☐ Can't win 'em all.
☐ You couldn't have known.
☐ My cousin had that and was fine.
☐ Laughter is the best medicine.
☐ Have faith.
☐ Penicillin clears that up fast.
☐ He wasn't thinking.
☐ She wasn't thinking.
☐ If at first you don't succeed . . .
☐ It's about quality, not quantity.
☐ That's not old, it's vintage.
☐ You're not old, you're vintage.
☐ Things happen for a reason.
☐ It'll look better in the morning.
☐ You can blog about it.
☐ We'll look back later and laugh.
☐ No one will ever know.
☐ Here's a hug.
☐ They don't deserve you.
☐ Every cloud has a silver lining.
☐ It was totally his fault.
☐ It was totally her fault.
☐ A rising tide lifts all boats.
☐ There are specialists for that.
☐ Think of the big picture.
☐ Don't let it bother you so much.
☐ No one saw you trip.
☐ You'll get that promotion soon.
☐ It could've been much worse.
☐ Aim for the stars.
☐ You'll forget about it, I promise.

☐ All publicity is good publicity.
☐ You can always return it.
☐ That was so understandable.
☐ You look great.
☐ You look great for your age.
☐ That happens to everyone.
☐ You made your point.
☐ Who wants that responsibility?
☐ It's not more than you can handle.
☐ Time heals all wounds.
☐ Time wounds all heels.
☐ I'm sure you don't normally do that.
☐ Success or not, you are loved.
☐ It's a journey, not a destination.
☐ It was a long shot anyway.
☐ Lesson learned.
☐ It's not you, it's the economy.
☐ You can always sue.
☐ You're the bigger person.
☐ You still have your honor.
☐ You still have your hair.
☐ Heartbreak makes you wiser.
☐ People will see through that.
☐ You'll be the last one standing.
☐ Don't let it get you down.
☐ It's not forever.
☐ There are always people like that.
☐ Never fear, karma's a bitch.
☐ I think it looks cute.
☐ One door closes, another opens.
☐ It's all part of the plan.
☐ Go ahead, cry it out.
☐ They spelled your name right.
☐ Jobs come, jobs go.
☐ People come, people go.
☐ This must be hard for you.
☐ Time to get on with your life.
☐ Everyone's a critic.
☐ It's for the best.
☐ Don't go there.
☐ It's their loss.
☐ You can focus on your career.
☐ You can focus on your kids.
☐ Didn't kill ya; made ya stronger.
☐ Ours is not to reason why.
☐ Don't take it home with you.
☐ Timing is everything.
☐ You'll eventually love it.
☐ Think positive.
☐ Think denial.

☐ Someday you'll understand.
☐ Single life is actually better.
☐ Always darkest before the dawn.
☐ Just clear the browser history.
☐ You're still young.
☐ He isn't worth it.
☐ She isn't worth it.
☐ Where there's a will . . .
☐ Chalk it up to experience.
☐ Cross that bridge later.
☐ One day at a time.
☐ You can always get it fixed.
☐ Don't sweat the small stuff.
☐ Not over 'til the fat lady sings.
☐ It's all nonsense anyway.
☐ You gotta believe in you.
☐ I believe in you.
☐ Anything is possible.
☐ You reacted with integrity.
☐ You can sell it online.
☐ Don't get mad, get even.
☐ No one can tell it's a knockoff.
☐ Just say no.
☐ Hang in there, baby.
☐ If it's not one thing, it's another.
☐ It'll build character.
☐ It was meant to be.
☐ It wasn't meant to be.
☐ If it's meant to be, it'll happen.
☐ Keep your chin up.
☐ You don't need their approval.
☐ For every hill there's a valley.
☐ I would've done the same.
☐ Life goes on.
☐ Absence makes love stronger.
☐ Can't beat 'em? Join 'em.
☐ Shake it off.
☐ No one heard it.
☐ Better late than never.
☐ Better safe than sorry.
☐ And so it goes.
☐ The first cut is the deepest.
☐ Love hurts.
☐ Love stinks.
☐ Love is overrated.
☐ Soon this'll be a distant memory.
☐ Keep on truckin'.
☐ Quit worrying.
☐ It's water under the bridge.
☐ Don't dwell on it.

☐ Ya gotta do what ya gotta do.
☐ When it rains, it pours.
☐ Every rose has a thorn.
☐ You gave it your best shot.
☐ There, there.
☐ It takes all kinds.
☐ They're just jealous.
☐ It'll come when you're ready.
☐ Nobody mentioned it.
☐ Try to keep it in perspective.
☐ Put on your big girl panties.
☐ Put on your big boy briefs.
☐ There's a lid for every pot.
☐ He's probably out of town.
☐ Her phone is probably dead.
☐ You're better off.
☐ It happens sometimes.
☐ They don't understand you.
☐ It was an honest mistake.
☐ Money can't buy love.
☐ Adversity forges character.
☐ You'll feel better after a bath.
☐ You'll feel better after a drink.
☐ It'll make great memoir material.
☐ Quit blaming yourself.
☐ There's no such thing as normal.
☐ You'll show them.
☐ This will forge your character.
☐ You're a superstar.
☐ Just explain what happened.
☐ Don't compare.
☐ All parents screw up.
☐ All kids screw up.
☐ At least you have your health.
☐ He'll grow out of it.
☐ She'll grow out of it.
☐ Shhh. Shhh. It's okay now.
☐ Pain is temporary.
☐ I agree with you.
☐ One day you'll know why.
☐ You march to your own beat.
☐ Ignore what others think.
☐ Buck up, buckwheat.
☐ Everyone sympathizes.
☐ You're overthinking this.
☐ Get back up on the horse.
☐ Just give it some time.
☐ It's not the end of the world.
☐ It gets better.
☐ Really, it is.

☐ **TOTALLY OKAY** ☐ **PRETTY OKAY** ☐ **OKAY-ISH**

SIGNATURE MONTH DAY YEAR

"OKAY? OKAY. OKAY!"

IT'S GONNA BE OKAY

☐ **RIGHT NOW** ☐ **FAIRLY SOON** ☐ **EVENTUALLY**

☐ It'll grow back.
☐ You'll get over it.
☐ You can do this.
☐ It wasn't that obvious.
☐ This too shall pass.
☐ You're too good for him.
☐ You're too good for her.
☐ I'll never tell.
☐ Don't blame yourself.
☐ There are other fish in the sea.
☐ Tattoo removal is easier now.
☐ You are not your job.
☐ Your mother will never know.
☐ Nothing therapy won't cure.
☐ Just take a mulligan.
☐ Moving home is no big deal.
☐ Don't "should" all over yourself.
☐ At least you know you're right.
☐ You did your best.
☐ Can't win 'em all.
☐ You couldn't have known.
☐ My cousin had that and was fine.
☐ Laughter is the best medicine.
☐ Have faith.
☐ Penicillin clears that up fast.
☐ He wasn't thinking.
☐ She wasn't thinking.
☐ If at first you don't succeed . . .
☐ It's about quality, not quantity.
☐ That's not old, it's vintage.
☐ You're not old, you're vintage.
☐ Things happen for a reason.
☐ It'll look better in the morning.
☐ You can blog about it.
☐ We'll look back later and laugh.
☐ No one will ever know.
☐ Here's a hug.
☐ They don't deserve you.
☐ Every cloud has a silver lining.
☐ It was totally his fault.
☐ It was totally her fault.
☐ A rising tide lifts all boats.
☐ There are specialists for that.
☐ Think of the big picture.
☐ Don't let it bother you so much.
☐ No one saw you trip.
☐ You'll get that promotion soon.
☐ It could've been much worse.
☐ Aim for the stars.
☐ You'll forget about it, I promise.

☐ All publicity is good publicity.
☐ You can always return it.
☐ That was so understandable.
☐ You look great.
☐ You look great for your age.
☐ That happens to everyone.
☐ You made your point.
☐ Who wants that responsibility?
☐ It's not more than you can handle.
☐ Time heals all wounds.
☐ Time wounds all heels.
☐ I'm sure you don't normally do that.
☐ Success or not, you are loved.
☐ It's a journey, not a destination.
☐ It was a long shot anyway.
☐ Lesson learned.
☐ It's not you, it's the economy.
☐ You can always sue.
☐ You're the bigger person.
☐ You still have your honor.
☐ You still have your hair.
☐ Heartbreak makes you wiser.
☐ People will see through that.
☐ You'll be the last one standing.
☐ Don't let it get you down.
☐ It's not forever.
☐ There are always people like that.
☐ Never fear, karma's a bitch.
☐ I think it looks cute.
☐ One door closes, another opens.
☐ It's all part of the plan.
☐ Go ahead, cry it out.
☐ They spelled your name right.
☐ Jobs come, jobs go.
☐ People come, people go.
☐ This must be hard for you.
☐ Time to get on with your life.
☐ Everyone's a critic.
☐ It's for the best.
☐ Don't go there.
☐ It's their loss.
☐ You can focus on your career.
☐ You can focus on your kids.
☐ Didn't kill ya; made ya stronger.
☐ Ours is not to reason why.
☐ Don't take it home with you.
☐ Timing is everything.
☐ You'll eventually love it.
☐ Think positive.
☐ Think denial.

☐ Someday you'll understand.
☐ Single life is actually better.
☐ Always darkest before the dawn.
☐ Just clear the browser history.
☐ You're still young.
☐ He isn't worth it.
☐ She isn't worth it.
☐ Where there's a will . . .
☐ Chalk it up to experience.
☐ Cross that bridge later.
☐ One day at a time.
☐ You can always get it fixed.
☐ Don't sweat the small stuff.
☐ Not over 'til the fat lady sings.
☐ It's all nonsense anyway.
☐ You gotta believe in you.
☐ I believe in you.
☐ Anything is possible.
☐ You reacted with integrity.
☐ You can sell it online.
☐ Don't get mad, get even.
☐ No one can tell it's a knockoff.
☐ Just say no.
☐ Hang in there, baby.
☐ If it's not one thing, it's another.
☐ It'll build character.
☐ It was meant to be.
☐ It wasn't meant to be.
☐ If it's meant to be, it'll happen.
☐ Keep your chin up.
☐ You don't need their approval.
☐ For every hill there's a valley.
☐ I would've done the same.
☐ Life goes on.
☐ Absence makes love stronger.
☐ Can't beat 'em? Join 'em.
☐ Shake it off.
☐ No one heard it.
☐ Better late than never.
☐ Better safe than sorry.
☐ And so it goes.
☐ The first cut is the deepest.
☐ Love hurts.
☐ Love stinks.
☐ Love is overrated.
☐ Soon this'll be a distant memory.
☐ Keep on truckin'.
☐ Quit worrying.
☐ It's water under the bridge.
☐ Don't dwell on it.

☐ Ya gotta do what ya gotta do.
☐ When it rains, it pours.
☐ Every rose has a thorn.
☐ You gave it your best shot.
☐ There, there.
☐ It takes all kinds.
☐ They're just jealous.
☐ It'll come when you're ready.
☐ Nobody mentioned it.
☐ Try to keep it in perspective.
☐ Put on your big girl panties.
☐ Put on your big boy briefs.
☐ There's a lid for every pot.
☐ He's probably out of town.
☐ Her phone is probably dead.
☐ You're better off.
☐ It happens sometimes.
☐ They don't understand you.
☐ It was an honest mistake.
☐ Money can't buy love.
☐ Adversity forges character.
☐ You'll feel better after a bath.
☐ You'll feel better after a drink.
☐ It'll make great memoir material.
☐ Quit blaming yourself.
☐ There's no such thing as normal.
☐ You'll show them.
☐ This will forge your character.
☐ You're a superstar.
☐ Just explain what happened.
☐ Don't compare.
☐ All parents screw up.
☐ All kids screw up.
☐ At least you have your health.
☐ He'll grow out of it.
☐ She'll grow out of it.
☐ Shhh. Shhh. It's okay now.
☐ Pain is temporary.
☐ I agree with you.
☐ One day you'll know why.
☐ You march to your own beat.
☐ Ignore what others think.
☐ Buck up, buckwheat.
☐ Everyone sympathizes.
☐ You're overthinking this.
☐ Get back up on the horse.
☐ Just give it some time.
☐ It's not the end of the world.
☐ It gets better.
☐ Really, it is.

☐ **TOTALLY OKAY** ☐ **PRETTY OKAY** ☐ **OKAY-ISH**

SIGNATURE MONTH DAY YEAR

"OKAY? OKAY. OKAY!"

IT'S GONNA BE OKAY

☐ **RIGHT NOW** ☐ **FAIRLY SOON** ☐ **EVENTUALLY**

☐ It'll grow back.
☐ You'll get over it.
☐ You can do this.
☐ It wasn't that obvious.
☐ This too shall pass.
☐ You're too good for him.
☐ You're too good for her.
☐ I'll never tell.
☐ Don't blame yourself.
☐ There are other fish in the sea.
☐ Tattoo removal is easier now.
☐ You are not your job.
☐ Your mother will never know.
☐ Nothing therapy won't cure.
☐ Just take a mulligan.
☐ Moving home is no big deal.
☐ Don't "should" all over yourself.
☐ At least you know you're right.
☐ You did your best.
☐ Can't win 'em all.
☐ You couldn't have known.
☐ My cousin had that and was fine.
☐ Laughter is the best medicine.
☐ Have faith.
☐ Penicillin clears that up fast.
☐ He wasn't thinking.
☐ She wasn't thinking.
☐ If at first you don't succeed . . .
☐ It's about quality, not quantity.
☐ That's not old, it's vintage.
☐ You're not old, you're vintage.
☐ Things happen for a reason.
☐ It'll look better in the morning.
☐ You can blog about it.
☐ We'll look back later and laugh.
☐ No one will ever know.
☐ Here's a hug.
☐ They don't deserve you.
☐ Every cloud has a silver lining.
☐ It was totally his fault.
☐ It was totally her fault.
☐ A rising tide lifts all boats.
☐ There are specialists for that.
☐ Think of the big picture.
☐ Don't let it bother you so much.
☐ No one saw you trip.
☐ You'll get that promotion soon.
☐ It could've been much worse.
☐ Aim for the stars.
☐ You'll forget about it, I promise.

☐ All publicity is good publicity.
☐ You can always return it.
☐ That was so understandable.
☐ You look great.
☐ You look great for your age.
☐ That happens to everyone.
☐ You made your point.
☐ Who wants that responsibility?
☐ It's not more than you can handle.
☐ Time heals all wounds.
☐ Time wounds all heels.
☐ I'm sure you don't normally do that.
☐ Success or not, you are loved.
☐ It's a journey, not a destination.
☐ It was a long shot anyway.
☐ Lesson learned.
☐ It's not you, it's the economy.
☐ You can always sue.
☐ You're the bigger person.
☐ You still have your honor.
☐ You still have your hair.
☐ Heartbreak makes you wiser.
☐ People will see through that.
☐ You'll be the last one standing.
☐ Don't let it get you down.
☐ It's not forever.
☐ There are always people like that.
☐ Never fear, karma's a bitch.
☐ I think it looks cute.
☐ One door closes, another opens.
☐ It's all part of the plan.
☐ Go ahead, cry it out.
☐ They spelled your name right.
☐ Jobs come, jobs go.
☐ People come, people go.
☐ This must be hard for you.
☐ Time to get on with your life.
☐ Everyone's a critic.
☐ It's for the best.
☐ Don't go there.
☐ It's their loss.
☐ You can focus on your career.
☐ You can focus on your kids.
☐ Didn't kill ya; made ya stronger.
☐ Ours is not to reason why.
☐ Don't take it home with you.
☐ Timing is everything.
☐ You'll eventually love it.
☐ Think positive.
☐ Think denial.

☐ Someday you'll understand.
☐ Single life is actually better.
☐ Always darkest before the dawn.
☐ Just clear the browser history.
☐ You're still young.
☐ He isn't worth it.
☐ She isn't worth it.
☐ Where there's a will . . .
☐ Chalk it up to experience.
☐ Cross that bridge later.
☐ One day at a time.
☐ You can always get it fixed.
☐ Don't sweat the small stuff.
☐ Not over 'til the fat lady sings.
☐ It's all nonsense anyway.
☐ You gotta believe in you.
☐ I believe in you.
☐ Anything is possible.
☐ You reacted with integrity.
☐ You can sell it online.
☐ Don't get mad, get even.
☐ No one can tell it's a knockoff.
☐ Just say no.
☐ Hang in there, baby.
☐ If it's not one thing, it's another.
☐ It'll build character.
☐ It was meant to be.
☐ It wasn't meant to be.
☐ If it's meant to be, it'll happen.
☐ Keep your chin up.
☐ You don't need their approval.
☐ For every hill there's a valley.
☐ I would've done the same.
☐ Life goes on.
☐ Absence makes love stronger.
☐ Can't beat 'em? Join 'em.
☐ Shake it off.
☐ No one heard it.
☐ Better late than never.
☐ Better safe than sorry.
☐ And so it goes.
☐ The first cut is the deepest.
☐ Love hurts.
☐ Love stinks.
☐ Love is overrated.
☐ Soon this'll be a distant memory.
☐ Keep on truckin'.
☐ Quit worrying.
☐ It's water under the bridge.
☐ Don't dwell on it.

☐ Ya gotta do what ya gotta do.
☐ When it rains, it pours.
☐ Every rose has a thorn.
☐ You gave it your best shot.
☐ There, there.
☐ It takes all kinds.
☐ They're just jealous.
☐ It'll come when you're ready.
☐ Nobody mentioned it.
☐ Try to keep it in perspective.
☐ Put on your big girl panties.
☐ Put on your big boy briefs.
☐ There's a lid for every pot.
☐ He's probably out of town.
☐ Her phone is probably dead.
☐ You're better off.
☐ It happens sometimes.
☐ They don't understand you.
☐ It was an honest mistake.
☐ Money can't buy love.
☐ Adversity forges character.
☐ You'll feel better after a bath.
☐ You'll feel better after a drink.
☐ It'll make great memoir material.
☐ Quit blaming yourself.
☐ There's no such thing as normal.
☐ You'll show them.
☐ This will forge your character.
☐ You're a superstar.
☐ Just explain what happened.
☐ Don't compare.
☐ All parents screw up.
☐ All kids screw up.
☐ At least you have your health.
☐ He'll grow out of it.
☐ She'll grow out of it.
☐ Shhh. Shhh. It's okay now.
☐ Pain is temporary.
☐ I agree with you.
☐ One day you'll know why.
☐ You march to your own beat.
☐ Ignore what others think.
☐ Buck up, buckwheat.
☐ Everyone sympathizes.
☐ You're overthinking this.
☐ Get back up on the horse.
☐ Just give it some time.
☐ It's not the end of the world.
☐ It gets better.
☐ Really, it is.

☐ **TOTALLY OKAY** ☐ **PRETTY OKAY** ☐ **OKAY-ISH**

SIGNATURE MONTH DAY YEAR

"OKAY? OKAY. OKAY!"

IT'S GONNA BE OKAY

☐ RIGHT NOW ☐ FAIRLY SOON ☐ EVENTUALLY

☐ It'll grow back.
☐ You'll get over it.
☐ You can do this.
☐ It wasn't that obvious.
☐ This too shall pass.
☐ You're too good for him.
☐ You're too good for her.
☐ I'll never tell.
☐ Don't blame yourself.
☐ There are other fish in the sea.
☐ Tattoo removal is easier now.
☐ You are not your job.
☐ Your mother will never know.
☐ Nothing therapy won't cure.
☐ Just take a mulligan.
☐ Moving home is no big deal.
☐ Don't "should" all over yourself.
☐ At least you know you're right.
☐ You did your best.
☐ Can't win 'em all.
☐ You couldn't have known.
☐ My cousin had that and was fine.
☐ Laughter is the best medicine.
☐ Have faith.
☐ Penicillin clears that up fast.
☐ He wasn't thinking.
☐ She wasn't thinking.
☐ If at first you don't succeed . . .
☐ It's about quality, not quantity.
☐ That's not old, it's vintage.
☐ You're not old, you're vintage.
☐ Things happen for a reason.
☐ It'll look better in the morning.
☐ You can blog about it.
☐ We'll look back later and laugh.
☐ No one will ever know.
☐ Here's a hug.
☐ They don't deserve you.
☐ Every cloud has a silver lining.
☐ It was totally his fault.
☐ It was totally her fault.
☐ A rising tide lifts all boats.
☐ There are specialists for that.
☐ Think of the big picture.
☐ Don't let it bother you so much.
☐ No one saw you trip.
☐ You'll get that promotion soon.
☐ It could've been much worse.
☐ Aim for the stars.
☐ You'll forget about it, I promise.

☐ All publicity is good publicity.
☐ You can always return it.
☐ That was so understandable.
☐ You look great.
☐ You look great for your age.
☐ That happens to everyone.
☐ You made your point.
☐ Who wants that responsibility?
☐ It's not more than you can handle.
☐ Time heals all wounds.
☐ Time wounds all heels.
☐ I'm sure you don't normally do that.
☐ Success or not, you are loved.
☐ It's a journey, not a destination.
☐ It was a long shot anyway.
☐ Lesson learned.
☐ It's not you, it's the economy.
☐ You can always sue.
☐ You're the bigger person.
☐ You still have your honor.
☐ You still have your hair.
☐ Heartbreak makes you wiser.
☐ People will see through that.
☐ You'll be the last one standing.
☐ Don't let it get you down.
☐ It's not forever.
☐ There are always people like that.
☐ Never fear, karma's a bitch.
☐ I think it looks cute.
☐ One door closes, another opens.
☐ It's all part of the plan.
☐ Go ahead, cry it out.
☐ They spelled your name right.
☐ Jobs come, jobs go.
☐ People come, people go.
☐ This must be hard for you.
☐ Time to get on with your life.
☐ Everyone's a critic.
☐ It's for the best.
☐ Don't go there.
☐ It's their loss.
☐ You can focus on your career.
☐ You can focus on your kids.
☐ Didn't kill ya; made ya stronger.
☐ Ours is not to reason why.
☐ Don't take it home with you.
☐ Timing is everything.
☐ You'll eventually love it.
☐ Think positive.
☐ Think denial.

☐ Someday you'll understand.
☐ Single life is actually better.
☐ Always darkest before the dawn.
☐ Just clear the browser history.
☐ You're still young.
☐ He isn't worth it.
☐ She isn't worth it.
☐ Where there's a will . . .
☐ Chalk it up to experience.
☐ Cross that bridge later.
☐ One day at a time.
☐ You can always get it fixed.
☐ Don't sweat the small stuff.
☐ Not over 'til the fat lady sings.
☐ It's all nonsense anyway.
☐ You gotta believe in you.
☐ I believe in you.
☐ Anything is possible.
☐ You reacted with integrity.
☐ You can sell it online.
☐ Don't get mad, get even.
☐ No one can tell it's a knockoff.
☐ Just say no.
☐ Hang in there, baby.
☐ If it's not one thing, it's another.
☐ It'll build character.
☐ It was meant to be.
☐ It wasn't meant to be.
☐ If it's meant to be, it'll happen.
☐ Keep your chin up.
☐ You don't need their approval.
☐ For every hill there's a valley.
☐ I would've done the same.
☐ Life goes on.
☐ Absence makes love stronger.
☐ Can't beat 'em? Join 'em.
☐ Shake it off.
☐ No one heard it.
☐ Better late than never.
☐ Better safe than sorry.
☐ And so it goes.
☐ The first cut is the deepest.
☐ Love hurts.
☐ Love stinks.
☐ Love is overrated.
☐ Soon this'll be a distant memory.
☐ Keep on truckin'.
☐ Quit worrying.
☐ It's water under the bridge.
☐ Don't dwell on it.

☐ Ya gotta do what ya gotta do.
☐ When it rains, it pours.
☐ Every rose has a thorn.
☐ You gave it your best shot.
☐ There, there.
☐ It takes all kinds.
☐ They're just jealous.
☐ It'll come when you're ready.
☐ Nobody mentioned it.
☐ Try to keep it in perspective.
☐ Put on your big girl panties.
☐ Put on your big boy briefs.
☐ There's a lid for every pot.
☐ He's probably out of town.
☐ Her phone is probably dead.
☐ You're better off.
☐ It happens sometimes.
☐ They don't understand you.
☐ It was an honest mistake.
☐ Money can't buy love.
☐ Adversity forges character.
☐ You'll feel better after a bath.
☐ You'll feel better after a drink.
☐ It'll make great memoir material.
☐ Quit blaming yourself.
☐ There's no such thing as normal.
☐ You'll show them.
☐ This will forge your character.
☐ You're a superstar.
☐ Just explain what happened.
☐ Don't compare.
☐ All parents screw up.
☐ All kids screw up.
☐ At least you have your health.
☐ He'll grow out of it.
☐ She'll grow out of it.
☐ Shhh. Shhh. It's okay now.
☐ Pain is temporary.
☐ I agree with you.
☐ One day you'll know why.
☐ You march to your own beat.
☐ Ignore what others think.
☐ Buck up, buckwheat.
☐ Everyone sympathizes.
☐ You're overthinking this.
☐ Get back up on the horse.
☐ Just give it some time.
☐ It's not the end of the world.
☐ It gets better.
☐ Really, it is.

☐ TOTALLY OKAY ☐ PRETTY OKAY ☐ OKAY-ISH

SIGNATURE MONTH DAY YEAR

"OKAY? OKAY. OKAY!"

IT'S GONNA BE OKAY

☐ **RIGHT NOW** ☐ **FAIRLY SOON** ☐ **EVENTUALLY**

☐ It'll grow back.
☐ You'll get over it.
☐ You can do this.
☐ It wasn't that obvious.
☐ This too shall pass.
☐ You're too good for him.
☐ You're too good for her.
☐ I'll never tell.
☐ Don't blame yourself.
☐ There are other fish in the sea.
☐ Tattoo removal is easier now.
☐ You are not your job.
☐ Your mother will never know.
☐ Nothing therapy won't cure.
☐ Just take a mulligan.
☐ Moving home is no big deal.
☐ Don't "should" all over yourself.
☐ At least you know you're right.
☐ You did your best.
☐ Can't win 'em all.
☐ You couldn't have known.
☐ My cousin had that and was fine.
☐ Laughter is the best medicine.
☐ Have faith.
☐ Penicillin clears that up fast.
☐ He wasn't thinking.
☐ She wasn't thinking.
☐ If at first you don't succeed . . .
☐ It's about quality, not quantity.
☐ That's not old, it's vintage.
☐ You're not old, you're vintage.
☐ Things happen for a reason.
☐ It'll look better in the morning.
☐ You can blog about it.
☐ We'll look back later and laugh.
☐ No one will ever know.
☐ Here's a hug.
☐ They don't deserve you.
☐ Every cloud has a silver lining.
☐ It was totally his fault.
☐ It was totally her fault.
☐ A rising tide lifts all boats.
☐ There are specialists for that.
☐ Think of the big picture.
☐ Don't let it bother you so much.
☐ No one saw you trip.
☐ You'll get that promotion soon.
☐ It could've been much worse.
☐ Aim for the stars.
☐ You'll forget about it, I promise.

☐ All publicity is good publicity.
☐ You can always return it.
☐ That was so understandable.
☐ You look great.
☐ You look great for your age.
☐ That happens to everyone.
☐ You made your point.
☐ Who wants that responsibility?
☐ It's not more than you can handle.
☐ Time heals all wounds.
☐ Time wounds all heels.
☐ I'm sure you don't normally do that.
☐ Success or not, you are loved.
☐ It's a journey, not a destination.
☐ It was a long shot anyway.
☐ Lesson learned.
☐ It's not you, it's the economy.
☐ You can always sue.
☐ You're the bigger person.
☐ You still have your honor.
☐ You still have your hair.
☐ Heartbreak makes you wiser.
☐ People will see through that.
☐ You'll be the last one standing.
☐ Don't let it get you down.
☐ It's not forever.
☐ There are always people like that.
☐ Never fear, karma's a bitch.
☐ I think it looks cute.
☐ One door closes, another opens.
☐ It's all part of the plan.
☐ Go ahead, cry it out.
☐ They spelled your name right.
☐ Jobs come, jobs go.
☐ People come, people go.
☐ This must be hard for you.
☐ Time to get on with your life.
☐ Everyone's a critic.
☐ It's for the best.
☐ Don't go there.
☐ It's their loss.
☐ You can focus on your career.
☐ You can focus on your kids.
☐ Didn't kill ya; made ya stronger.
☐ Ours is not to reason why.
☐ Don't take it home with you.
☐ Timing is everything.
☐ You'll eventually love it.
☐ Think positive.
☐ Think denial.

☐ Someday you'll understand.
☐ Single life is actually better.
☐ Always darkest before the dawn.
☐ Just clear the browser history.
☐ You're still young.
☐ He isn't worth it.
☐ She isn't worth it.
☐ Where there's a will . . .
☐ Chalk it up to experience.
☐ Cross that bridge later.
☐ One day at a time.
☐ You can always get it fixed.
☐ Don't sweat the small stuff.
☐ Not over 'til the fat lady sings.
☐ It's all nonsense anyway.
☐ You gotta believe in you.
☐ I believe in you.
☐ Anything is possible.
☐ You reacted with integrity.
☐ You can sell it online.
☐ Don't get mad, get even.
☐ No one can tell it's a knockoff.
☐ Just say no.
☐ Hang in there, baby.
☐ If it's not one thing, it's another.
☐ It'll build character.
☐ It was meant to be.
☐ It wasn't meant to be.
☐ If it's meant to be, it'll happen.
☐ Keep your chin up.
☐ You don't need their approval.
☐ For every hill there's a valley.
☐ I would've done the same.
☐ Life goes on.
☐ Absence makes love stronger.
☐ Can't beat 'em? Join 'em.
☐ Shake it off.
☐ No one heard it.
☐ Better late than never.
☐ Better safe than sorry.
☐ And so it goes.
☐ The first cut is the deepest.
☐ Love hurts.
☐ Love stinks.
☐ Love is overrated.
☐ Soon this'll be a distant memory.
☐ Keep on truckin'.
☐ Quit worrying.
☐ It's water under the bridge.
☐ Don't dwell on it.

☐ Ya gotta do what ya gotta do.
☐ When it rains, it pours.
☐ Every rose has a thorn.
☐ You gave it your best shot.
☐ There, there.
☐ It takes all kinds.
☐ They're just jealous.
☐ It'll come when you're ready.
☐ Nobody mentioned it.
☐ Try to keep it in perspective.
☐ Put on your big girl panties.
☐ Put on your big boy briefs.
☐ There's a lid for every pot.
☐ He's probably out of town.
☐ Her phone is probably dead.
☐ You're better off.
☐ It happens sometimes.
☐ They don't understand you.
☐ It was an honest mistake.
☐ Money can't buy love.
☐ Adversity forges character.
☐ You'll feel better after a bath.
☐ You'll feel better after a drink.
☐ It'll make great memoir material.
☐ Quit blaming yourself.
☐ There's no such thing as normal.
☐ You'll show them.
☐ This will forge your character.
☐ You're a superstar.
☐ Just explain what happened.
☐ Don't compare.
☐ All parents screw up.
☐ All kids screw up.
☐ At least you have your health.
☐ He'll grow out of it.
☐ She'll grow out of it.
☐ Shhh. Shhh. It's okay now.
☐ Pain is temporary.
☐ I agree with you.
☐ One day you'll know why.
☐ You march to your own beat.
☐ Ignore what others think.
☐ Buck up, buckwheat.
☐ Everyone sympathizes.
☐ You're overthinking this.
☐ Get back up on the horse.
☐ Just give it some time.
☐ It's not the end of the world.
☐ It gets better.
☐ Really, it is.

☐ **TOTALLY OKAY** ☐ **PRETTY OKAY** ☐ **OKAY-ISH**

SIGNATURE MONTH DAY YEAR

"OKAY? OKAY. OKAY!"

IT'S GONNA BE OKAY

☐ **RIGHT NOW** ☐ **FAIRLY SOON** ☐ **EVENTUALLY**

☐ It'll grow back.
☐ You'll get over it.
☐ You can do this.
☐ It wasn't that obvious.
☐ This too shall pass.
☐ You're too good for him.
☐ You're too good for her.
☐ I'll never tell.
☐ Don't blame yourself.
☐ There are other fish in the sea.
☐ Tattoo removal is easier now.
☐ You are not your job.
☐ Your mother will never know.
☐ Nothing therapy won't cure.
☐ Just take a mulligan.
☐ Moving home is no big deal.
☐ Don't "should" all over yourself.
☐ At least you know you're right.
☐ You did your best.
☐ Can't win 'em all.
☐ You couldn't have known.
☐ My cousin had that and was fine.
☐ Laughter is the best medicine.
☐ Have faith.
☐ Penicillin clears that up fast.
☐ He wasn't thinking.
☐ She wasn't thinking.
☐ If at first you don't succeed . . .
☐ It's about quality, not quantity.
☐ That's not old, it's vintage.
☐ You're not old, you're vintage.
☐ Things happen for a reason.
☐ It'll look better in the morning.
☐ You can blog about it.
☐ We'll look back later and laugh.
☐ No one will ever know.
☐ Here's a hug.
☐ They don't deserve you.
☐ Every cloud has a silver lining.
☐ It was totally his fault.
☐ It was totally her fault.
☐ A rising tide lifts all boats.
☐ There are specialists for that.
☐ Think of the big picture.
☐ Don't let it bother you so much.
☐ No one saw you trip.
☐ You'll get that promotion soon.
☐ It could've been much worse.
☐ Aim for the stars.
☐ You'll forget about it, I promise.

☐ All publicity is good publicity.
☐ You can always return it.
☐ That was so understandable.
☐ You look great.
☐ You look great for your age.
☐ That happens to everyone.
☐ You made your point.
☐ Who wants that responsibility?
☐ It's not more than you can handle.
☐ Time heals all wounds.
☐ Time wounds all heels.
☐ I'm sure you don't normally do that.
☐ Success or not, you are loved.
☐ It's a journey, not a destination.
☐ It was a long shot anyway.
☐ Lesson learned.
☐ It's not you, it's the economy.
☐ You can always sue.
☐ You're the bigger person.
☐ You still have your honor.
☐ You still have your hair.
☐ Heartbreak makes you wiser.
☐ People will see through that.
☐ You'll be the last one standing.
☐ Don't let it get you down.
☐ It's not forever.
☐ There are always people like that.
☐ Never fear, karma's a bitch.
☐ I think it looks cute.
☐ One door closes, another opens.
☐ It's all part of the plan.
☐ Go ahead, cry it out.
☐ They spelled your name right.
☐ Jobs come, jobs go.
☐ People come, people go.
☐ This must be hard for you.
☐ Time to get on with your life.
☐ Everyone's a critic.
☐ It's for the best.
☐ Don't go there.
☐ It's their loss.
☐ You can focus on your career.
☐ You can focus on your kids.
☐ Didn't kill ya; made ya stronger.
☐ Ours is not to reason why.
☐ Don't take it home with you.
☐ Timing is everything.
☐ You'll eventually love it.
☐ Think positive.
☐ Think denial.

☐ Someday you'll understand.
☐ Single life is actually better.
☐ Always darkest before the dawn.
☐ Just clear the browser history.
☐ You're still young.
☐ He isn't worth it.
☐ She isn't worth it.
☐ Where there's a will . . .
☐ Chalk it up to experience.
☐ Cross that bridge later.
☐ One day at a time.
☐ You can always get it fixed.
☐ Don't sweat the small stuff.
☐ Not over 'til the fat lady sings.
☐ It's all nonsense anyway.
☐ You gotta believe in you.
☐ I believe in you.
☐ Anything is possible.
☐ You reacted with integrity.
☐ You can sell it online.
☐ Don't get mad, get even.
☐ No one can tell it's a knockoff.
☐ Just say no.
☐ Hang in there, baby.
☐ If it's not one thing, it's another.
☐ It'll build character.
☐ It was meant to be.
☐ It wasn't meant to be.
☐ If it's meant to be, it'll happen.
☐ Keep your chin up.
☐ You don't need their approval.
☐ For every hill there's a valley.
☐ I would've done the same.
☐ Life goes on.
☐ Absence makes love stronger.
☐ Can't beat 'em? Join 'em.
☐ Shake it off.
☐ No one heard it.
☐ Better late than never.
☐ Better safe than sorry.
☐ And so it goes.
☐ The first cut is the deepest.
☐ Love hurts.
☐ Love stinks.
☐ Love is overrated.
☐ Soon this'll be a distant memory.
☐ Keep on truckin'.
☐ Quit worrying.
☐ It's water under the bridge.
☐ Don't dwell on it.

☐ Ya gotta do what ya gotta do.
☐ When it rains, it pours.
☐ Every rose has a thorn.
☐ You gave it your best shot.
☐ There, there.
☐ It takes all kinds.
☐ They're just jealous.
☐ It'll come when you're ready.
☐ Nobody mentioned it.
☐ Try to keep it in perspective.
☐ Put on your big girl panties.
☐ Put on your big boy briefs.
☐ There's a lid for every pot.
☐ He's probably out of town.
☐ Her phone is probably dead.
☐ You're better off.
☐ It happens sometimes.
☐ They don't understand you.
☐ It was an honest mistake.
☐ Money can't buy love.
☐ Adversity forges character.
☐ You'll feel better after a bath.
☐ You'll feel better after a drink.
☐ It'll make great memoir material.
☐ Quit blaming yourself.
☐ There's no such thing as normal.
☐ You'll show them.
☐ This will forge your character.
☐ You're a superstar.
☐ Just explain what happened.
☐ Don't compare.
☐ All parents screw up.
☐ All kids screw up.
☐ At least you have your health.
☐ He'll grow out of it.
☐ She'll grow out of it.
☐ Shhh. Shhh. It's okay now.
☐ Pain is temporary.
☐ I agree with you.
☐ One day you'll know why.
☐ You march to your own beat.
☐ Ignore what others think.
☐ Buck up, buckwheat.
☐ Everyone sympathizes.
☐ You're overthinking this.
☐ Get back up on the horse.
☐ Just give it some time.
☐ It's not the end of the world.
☐ It gets better.
☐ Really, it is.

☐ **TOTALLY OKAY** ☐ **PRETTY OKAY** ☐ **OKAY-ISH**

SIGNATURE

MONTH DAY YEAR

"OKAY? OKAY. OKAY!"

IT'S GONNA BE OKAY

☐ RIGHT NOW ☐ FAIRLY SOON ☐ EVENTUALLY

- ☐ It'll grow back.
- ☐ You'll get over it.
- ☐ You can do this.
- ☐ It wasn't that obvious.
- ☐ This too shall pass.
- ☐ You're too good for him.
- ☐ You're too good for her.
- ☐ I'll never tell.
- ☐ Don't blame yourself.
- ☐ There are other fish in the sea.
- ☐ Tattoo removal is easier now.
- ☐ You are not your job.
- ☐ Your mother will never know.
- ☐ Nothing therapy won't cure.
- ☐ Just take a mulligan.
- ☐ Moving home is no big deal.
- ☐ Don't "should" all over yourself.
- ☐ At least you know you're right.
- ☐ You did your best.
- ☐ Can't win 'em all.
- ☐ You couldn't have known.
- ☐ My cousin had that and was fine.
- ☐ Laughter is the best medicine.
- ☐ Have faith.
- ☐ Penicillin clears that up fast.
- ☐ He wasn't thinking.
- ☐ She wasn't thinking.
- ☐ If at first you don't succeed . . .
- ☐ It's about quality, not quantity.
- ☐ That's not old, it's vintage.
- ☐ You're not old, you're vintage.
- ☐ Things happen for a reason.
- ☐ It'll look better in the morning.
- ☐ You can blog about it.
- ☐ We'll look back later and laugh.
- ☐ No one will ever know.
- ☐ Here's a hug.
- ☐ They don't deserve you.
- ☐ Every cloud has a silver lining.
- ☐ It was totally his fault.
- ☐ It was totally her fault.
- ☐ A rising tide lifts all boats.
- ☐ There are specialists for that.
- ☐ Think of the big picture.
- ☐ Don't let it bother you so much.
- ☐ No one saw you trip.
- ☐ You'll get that promotion soon.
- ☐ It could've been much worse.
- ☐ Aim for the stars.
- ☐ You'll forget about it, I promise.
- ☐ All publicity is good publicity.
- ☐ You can always return it.
- ☐ That was so understandable.
- ☐ You look great.
- ☐ You look great for your age.
- ☐ That happens to everyone.
- ☐ You made your point.
- ☐ Who wants that responsibility?
- ☐ It's not more than you can handle.
- ☐ Time heals all wounds.
- ☐ Time wounds all heels.
- ☐ I'm sure you don't normally do that.
- ☐ Success or not, you are loved.
- ☐ It's a journey, not a destination.
- ☐ It was a long shot anyway.
- ☐ Lesson learned.
- ☐ It's not you, it's the economy.
- ☐ You can always sue.
- ☐ You're the bigger person.
- ☐ You still have your honor.
- ☐ You still have your hair.
- ☐ Heartbreak makes you wiser.
- ☐ People will see through that.
- ☐ You'll be the last one standing.
- ☐ Don't let it get you down.
- ☐ It's not forever.
- ☐ There are always people like that.
- ☐ Never fear, karma's a bitch.
- ☐ I think it looks cute.
- ☐ One door closes, another opens.
- ☐ It's all part of the plan.
- ☐ Go ahead, cry it out.
- ☐ They spelled your name right.
- ☐ Jobs come, jobs go.
- ☐ People come, people go.
- ☐ This must be hard for you.
- ☐ Time to get on with your life.
- ☐ Everyone's a critic.
- ☐ It's for the best.
- ☐ Don't go there.
- ☐ It's their loss.
- ☐ You can focus on your career.
- ☐ You can focus on your kids.
- ☐ Didn't kill ya; made ya stronger.
- ☐ Ours is not to reason why.
- ☐ Don't take it home with you.
- ☐ Timing is everything.
- ☐ You'll eventually love it.
- ☐ Think positive.
- ☐ Think denial.
- ☐ Someday you'll understand.
- ☐ Single life is actually better.
- ☐ Always darkest before the dawn.
- ☐ Just clear the browser history.
- ☐ You're still young.
- ☐ He isn't worth it.
- ☐ She isn't worth it.
- ☐ Where there's a will . . .
- ☐ Chalk it up to experience.
- ☐ Cross that bridge later.
- ☐ One day at a time.
- ☐ You can always get it fixed.
- ☐ Don't sweat the small stuff.
- ☐ Not over 'til the fat lady sings.
- ☐ It's all nonsense anyway.
- ☐ You gotta believe in you.
- ☐ I believe in you.
- ☐ Anything is possible.
- ☐ You reacted with integrity.
- ☐ You can sell it online.
- ☐ Don't get mad, get even.
- ☐ No one can tell it's a knockoff.
- ☐ Just say no.
- ☐ Hang in there, baby.
- ☐ If it's not one thing, it's another.
- ☐ It'll build character.
- ☐ It was meant to be.
- ☐ It wasn't meant to be.
- ☐ If it's meant to be, it'll happen.
- ☐ Keep your chin up.
- ☐ You don't need their approval.
- ☐ For every hill there's a valley.
- ☐ I would've done the same.
- ☐ Life goes on.
- ☐ Absence makes love stronger.
- ☐ Can't beat 'em? Join 'em.
- ☐ Shake it off.
- ☐ No one heard it.
- ☐ Better late than never.
- ☐ Better safe than sorry.
- ☐ And so it goes.
- ☐ The first cut is the deepest.
- ☐ Love hurts.
- ☐ Love stinks.
- ☐ Love is overrated.
- ☐ Soon this'll be a distant memory.
- ☐ Keep on truckin'.
- ☐ Quit worrying.
- ☐ It's water under the bridge.
- ☐ Don't dwell on it.
- ☐ Ya gotta do what ya gotta do.
- ☐ When it rains, it pours.
- ☐ Every rose has a thorn.
- ☐ You gave it your best shot.
- ☐ There, there.
- ☐ It takes all kinds.
- ☐ They're just jealous.
- ☐ It'll come when you're ready.
- ☐ Nobody mentioned it.
- ☐ Try to keep it in perspective.
- ☐ Put on your big girl panties.
- ☐ Put on your big boy briefs.
- ☐ There's a lid for every pot.
- ☐ He's probably out of town.
- ☐ Her phone is probably dead.
- ☐ You're better off.
- ☐ It happens sometimes.
- ☐ They don't understand you.
- ☐ It was an honest mistake.
- ☐ Money can't buy love.
- ☐ Adversity forges character.
- ☐ You'll feel better after a bath.
- ☐ You'll feel better after a drink.
- ☐ It'll make great memoir material.
- ☐ Quit blaming yourself.
- ☐ There's no such thing as normal.
- ☐ You'll show them.
- ☐ This will forge your character.
- ☐ You're a superstar.
- ☐ Just explain what happened.
- ☐ Don't compare.
- ☐ All parents screw up.
- ☐ All kids screw up.
- ☐ At least you have your health.
- ☐ He'll grow out of it.
- ☐ She'll grow out of it.
- ☐ Shhh. Shhh. It's okay now.
- ☐ Pain is temporary.
- ☐ I agree with you.
- ☐ One day you'll know why.
- ☐ You march to your own beat.
- ☐ Ignore what others think.
- ☐ Buck up, buckwheat.
- ☐ Everyone sympathizes.
- ☐ You're overthinking this.
- ☐ Get back up on the horse.
- ☐ Just give it some time.
- ☐ It's not the end of the world.
- ☐ It gets better.
- ☐ Really, it is.

☐ TOTALLY OKAY ☐ PRETTY OKAY ☐ OKAY-ISH

SIGNATURE MONTH : DAY : YEAR

"OKAY? OKAY. OKAY!"

IT'S GONNA BE OKAY

☐ **RIGHT NOW** ☐ **FAIRLY SOON** ☐ **EVENTUALLY**

☐ It'll grow back.
☐ You'll get over it.
☐ You can do this.
☐ It wasn't that obvious.
☐ This too shall pass.
☐ You're too good for him.
☐ You're too good for her.
☐ I'll never tell.
☐ Don't blame yourself.
☐ There are other fish in the sea.
☐ Tattoo removal is easier now.
☐ You are not your job.
☐ Your mother will never know.
☐ Nothing therapy won't cure.
☐ Just take a mulligan.
☐ Moving home is no big deal.
☐ Don't "should" all over yourself.
☐ At least you know you're right.
☐ You did your best.
☐ Can't win 'em all.
☐ You couldn't have known.
☐ My cousin had that and was fine.
☐ Laughter is the best medicine.
☐ Have faith.
☐ Penicillin clears that up fast.
☐ He wasn't thinking.
☐ She wasn't thinking.
☐ If at first you don't succeed . . .
☐ It's about quality, not quantity.
☐ That's not old, it's vintage.
☐ You're not old, you're vintage.
☐ Things happen for a reason.
☐ It'll look better in the morning.
☐ You can blog about it.
☐ We'll look back later and laugh.
☐ No one will ever know.
☐ Here's a hug.
☐ They don't deserve you.
☐ Every cloud has a silver lining.
☐ It was totally his fault.
☐ It was totally her fault.
☐ A rising tide lifts all boats.
☐ There are specialists for that.
☐ Think of the big picture.
☐ Don't let it bother you so much.
☐ No one saw you trip.
☐ You'll get that promotion soon.
☐ It could've been much worse.
☐ Aim for the stars.
☐ You'll forget about it, I promise.

☐ All publicity is good publicity.
☐ You can always return it.
☐ That was so understandable.
☐ You look great.
☐ You look great for your age.
☐ That happens to everyone.
☐ You made your point.
☐ Who wants that responsibility?
☐ It's not more than you can handle.
☐ Time heals all wounds.
☐ Time wounds all heels.
☐ I'm sure you don't normally do that.
☐ Success or not, you are loved.
☐ It's a journey, not a destination.
☐ It was a long shot anyway.
☐ Lesson learned.
☐ It's not you, it's the economy.
☐ You can always sue.
☐ You're the bigger person.
☐ You still have your honor.
☐ You still have your hair.
☐ Heartbreak makes you wiser.
☐ People will see through that.
☐ You'll be the last one standing.
☐ Don't let it get you down.
☐ It's not forever.
☐ There are always people like that.
☐ Never fear, karma's a bitch.
☐ I think it looks cute.
☐ One door closes, another opens.
☐ It's all part of the plan.
☐ Go ahead, cry it out.
☐ They spelled your name right.
☐ Jobs come, jobs go.
☐ People come, people go.
☐ This must be hard for you.
☐ Time to get on with your life.
☐ Everyone's a critic.
☐ It's for the best.
☐ Don't go there.
☐ It's their loss.
☐ You can focus on your career.
☐ You can focus on your kids.
☐ Didn't kill ya; made ya stronger.
☐ Ours is not to reason why.
☐ Don't take it home with you.
☐ Timing is everything.
☐ You'll eventually love it.
☐ Think positive.
☐ Think denial.

☐ Someday you'll understand.
☐ Single life is actually better.
☐ Always darkest before the dawn.
☐ Just clear the browser history.
☐ You're still young.
☐ He isn't worth it.
☐ She isn't worth it.
☐ Where there's a will . . .
☐ Chalk it up to experience.
☐ Cross that bridge later.
☐ One day at a time.
☐ You can always get it fixed.
☐ Don't sweat the small stuff.
☐ Not over 'til the fat lady sings.
☐ It's all nonsense anyway.
☐ You gotta believe in you.
☐ I believe in you.
☐ Anything is possible.
☐ You reacted with integrity.
☐ You can sell it online.
☐ Don't get mad, get even.
☐ No one can tell it's a knockoff.
☐ Just say no.
☐ Hang in there, baby.
☐ If it's not one thing, it's another.
☐ It'll build character.
☐ It was meant to be.
☐ It wasn't meant to be.
☐ If it's meant to be, it'll happen.
☐ Keep your chin up.
☐ You don't need their approval.
☐ For every hill there's a valley.
☐ I would've done the same.
☐ Life goes on.
☐ Absence makes love stronger.
☐ Can't beat 'em? Join 'em.
☐ Shake it off.
☐ No one heard it.
☐ Better late than never.
☐ Better safe than sorry.
☐ And so it goes.
☐ The first cut is the deepest.
☐ Love hurts.
☐ Love stinks.
☐ Love is overrated.
☐ Soon this'll be a distant memory.
☐ Keep on truckin'.
☐ Quit worrying.
☐ It's water under the bridge.
☐ Don't dwell on it.

☐ Ya gotta do what ya gotta do.
☐ When it rains, it pours.
☐ Every rose has a thorn.
☐ You gave it your best shot.
☐ There, there.
☐ It takes all kinds.
☐ They're just jealous.
☐ It'll come when you're ready.
☐ Nobody mentioned it.
☐ Try to keep it in perspective.
☐ Put on your big girl panties.
☐ Put on your big boy briefs.
☐ There's a lid for every pot.
☐ He's probably out of town.
☐ Her phone is probably dead.
☐ You're better off.
☐ It happens sometimes.
☐ They don't understand you.
☐ It was an honest mistake.
☐ Money can't buy love.
☐ Adversity forges character.
☐ You'll feel better after a bath.
☐ You'll feel better after a drink.
☐ It'll make great memoir material.
☐ Quit blaming yourself.
☐ There's no such thing as normal.
☐ You'll show them.
☐ This will forge your character.
☐ You're a superstar.
☐ Just explain what happened.
☐ Don't compare.
☐ All parents screw up.
☐ All kids screw up.
☐ At least you have your health.
☐ He'll grow out of it.
☐ She'll grow out of it.
☐ Shhh. Shhh. It's okay now.
☐ Pain is temporary.
☐ I agree with you.
☐ One day you'll know why.
☐ You march to your own beat.
☐ Ignore what others think.
☐ Buck up, buckwheat.
☐ Everyone sympathizes.
☐ You're overthinking this.
☐ Get back up on the horse.
☐ Just give it some time.
☐ It's not the end of the world.
☐ It gets better.
☐ Really, it is.

☐ **TOTALLY OKAY** ☐ **PRETTY OKAY** ☐ **OKAY-ISH**

SIGNATURE	MONTH	DAY	YEAR

"OKAY? OKAY. OKAY!"

IT'S GONNA BE OKAY

☐ **RIGHT NOW** ☐ **FAIRLY SOON** ☐ **EVENTUALLY**

☐ It'll grow back.
☐ You'll get over it.
☐ You can do this.
☐ It wasn't that obvious.
☐ This too shall pass.
☐ You're too good for him.
☐ You're too good for her.
☐ I'll never tell.
☐ Don't blame yourself.
☐ There are other fish in the sea.
☐ Tattoo removal is easier now.
☐ You are not your job.
☐ Your mother will never know.
☐ Nothing therapy won't cure.
☐ Just take a mulligan.
☐ Moving home is no big deal.
☐ Don't "should" all over yourself.
☐ At least you know you're right.
☐ You did your best.
☐ Can't win 'em all.
☐ You couldn't have known.
☐ My cousin had that and was fine.
☐ Laughter is the best medicine.
☐ Have faith.
☐ Penicillin clears that up fast.
☐ He wasn't thinking.
☐ She wasn't thinking.
☐ If at first you don't succeed . . .
☐ It's about quality, not quantity.
☐ That's not old, it's vintage.
☐ You're not old, you're vintage.
☐ Things happen for a reason.
☐ It'll look better in the morning.
☐ You can blog about it.
☐ We'll look back later and laugh.
☐ No one will ever know.
☐ Here's a hug.
☐ They don't deserve you.
☐ Every cloud has a silver lining.
☐ It was totally his fault.
☐ It was totally her fault.
☐ A rising tide lifts all boats.
☐ There are specialists for that.
☐ Think of the big picture.
☐ Don't let it bother you so much.
☐ No one saw you trip.
☐ You'll get that promotion soon.
☐ It could've been much worse.
☐ Aim for the stars.
☐ You'll forget about it, I promise.

☐ All publicity is good publicity.
☐ You can always return it.
☐ That was so understandable.
☐ You look great.
☐ You look great for your age.
☐ That happens to everyone.
☐ You made your point.
☐ Who wants that responsibility?
☐ It's not more than you can handle.
☐ Time heals all wounds.
☐ Time wounds all heels.
☐ I'm sure you don't normally do that.
☐ Success or not, you are loved.
☐ It's a journey, not a destination.
☐ It was a long shot anyway.
☐ Lesson learned.
☐ It's not you, it's the economy.
☐ You can always sue.
☐ You're the bigger person.
☐ You still have your honor.
☐ You still have your hair.
☐ Heartbreak makes you wiser.
☐ People will see through that.
☐ You'll be the last one standing.
☐ Don't let it get you down.
☐ It's not forever.
☐ There are always people like that.
☐ Never fear, karma's a bitch.
☐ I think it looks cute.
☐ One door closes, another opens.
☐ It's all part of the plan.
☐ Go ahead, cry it out.
☐ They spelled your name right.
☐ Jobs come, jobs go.
☐ People come, people go.
☐ This must be hard for you.
☐ Time to get on with your life.
☐ Everyone's a critic.
☐ It's for the best.
☐ Don't go there.
☐ It's their loss.
☐ You can focus on your career.
☐ You can focus on your kids.
☐ Didn't kill ya; made ya stronger.
☐ Ours is not to reason why.
☐ Don't take it home with you.
☐ Timing is everything.
☐ You'll eventually love it.
☐ Think positive.
☐ Think denial.

☐ Someday you'll understand.
☐ Single life is actually better.
☐ Always darkest before the dawn.
☐ Just clear the browser history.
☐ You're still young.
☐ He isn't worth it.
☐ She isn't worth it.
☐ Where there's a will . . .
☐ Chalk it up to experience.
☐ Cross that bridge later.
☐ One day at a time.
☐ You can always get it fixed.
☐ Don't sweat the small stuff.
☐ Not over 'til the fat lady sings.
☐ It's all nonsense anyway.
☐ You gotta believe in you.
☐ I believe in you.
☐ Anything is possible.
☐ You reacted with integrity.
☐ You can sell it online.
☐ Don't get mad, get even.
☐ No one can tell it's a knockoff.
☐ Just say no.
☐ Hang in there, baby.
☐ If it's not one thing, it's another.
☐ It'll build character.
☐ It was meant to be.
☐ It wasn't meant to be.
☐ If it's meant to be, it'll happen.
☐ Keep your chin up.
☐ You don't need their approval.
☐ For every hill there's a valley.
☐ I would've done the same.
☐ Life goes on.
☐ Absence makes love stronger.
☐ Can't beat 'em? Join 'em.
☐ Shake it off.
☐ No one heard it.
☐ Better late than never.
☐ Better safe than sorry.
☐ And so it goes.
☐ The first cut is the deepest.
☐ Love hurts.
☐ Love stinks.
☐ Love is overrated.
☐ Soon this'll be a distant memory.
☐ Keep on truckin'.
☐ Quit worrying.
☐ It's water under the bridge.
☐ Don't dwell on it.

☐ Ya gotta do what ya gotta do.
☐ When it rains, it pours.
☐ Every rose has a thorn.
☐ You gave it your best shot.
☐ There, there.
☐ It takes all kinds.
☐ They're just jealous.
☐ It'll come when you're ready.
☐ Nobody mentioned it.
☐ Try to keep it in perspective.
☐ Put on your big girl panties.
☐ Put on your big boy briefs.
☐ There's a lid for every pot.
☐ He's probably out of town.
☐ Her phone is probably dead.
☐ You're better off.
☐ It happens sometimes.
☐ They don't understand you.
☐ It was an honest mistake.
☐ Money can't buy love.
☐ Adversity forges character.
☐ You'll feel better after a bath.
☐ You'll feel better after a drink.
☐ It'll make great memoir material.
☐ Quit blaming yourself.
☐ There's no such thing as normal.
☐ You'll show them.
☐ This will forge your character.
☐ You're a superstar.
☐ Just explain what happened.
☐ Don't compare.
☐ All parents screw up.
☐ All kids screw up.
☐ At least you have your health.
☐ He'll grow out of it.
☐ She'll grow out of it.
☐ Shhh. Shhh. It's okay now.
☐ Pain is temporary.
☐ I agree with you.
☐ One day you'll know why.
☐ You march to your own beat.
☐ Ignore what others think.
☐ Buck up, buckwheat.
☐ Everyone sympathizes.
☐ You're overthinking this.
☐ Get back up on the horse.
☐ Just give it some time.
☐ It's not the end of the world.
☐ It gets better.
☐ Really, it is.

☐ **TOTALLY OKAY** ☐ **PRETTY OKAY** ☐ **OKAY-ISH**

SIGNATURE MONTH DAY YEAR

"OKAY? OKAY. OKAY!"

IT'S GONNA BE OKAY

☐ **RIGHT NOW** ☐ **FAIRLY SOON** ☐ **EVENTUALLY**

☐ It'll grow back.
☐ You'll get over it.
☐ You can do this.
☐ It wasn't that obvious.
☐ This too shall pass.
☐ You're too good for him.
☐ You're too good for her.
☐ I'll never tell.
☐ Don't blame yourself.
☐ There are other fish in the sea.
☐ Tattoo removal is easier now.
☐ You are not your job.
☐ Your mother will never know.
☐ Nothing therapy won't cure.
☐ Just take a mulligan.
☐ Moving home is no big deal.
☐ Don't "should" all over yourself.
☐ At least you know you're right.
☐ You did your best.
☐ Can't win 'em all.
☐ You couldn't have known.
☐ My cousin had that and was fine.
☐ Laughter is the best medicine.
☐ Have faith.
☐ Penicillin clears that up fast.
☐ He wasn't thinking.
☐ She wasn't thinking.
☐ If at first you don't succeed . . .
☐ It's about quality, not quantity.
☐ That's not old, it's vintage.
☐ You're not old, you're vintage.
☐ Things happen for a reason.
☐ It'll look better in the morning.
☐ You can blog about it.
☐ We'll look back later and laugh.
☐ No one will ever know.
☐ Here's a hug.
☐ They don't deserve you.
☐ Every cloud has a silver lining.
☐ It was totally his fault.
☐ It was totally her fault.
☐ A rising tide lifts all boats.
☐ There are specialists for that.
☐ Think of the big picture.
☐ Don't let it bother you so much.
☐ No one saw you trip.
☐ You'll get that promotion soon.
☐ It could've been much worse.
☐ Aim for the stars.
☐ You'll forget about it, I promise.

☐ All publicity is good publicity.
☐ You can always return it.
☐ That was so understandable.
☐ You look great.
☐ You look great for your age.
☐ That happens to everyone.
☐ You made your point.
☐ Who wants that responsibility?
☐ It's not more than you can handle.
☐ Time heals all wounds.
☐ Time wounds all heels.
☐ I'm sure you don't normally do that.
☐ Success or not, you are loved.
☐ It's a journey, not a destination.
☐ It was a long shot anyway.
☐ Lesson learned.
☐ It's not you, it's the economy.
☐ You can always sue.
☐ You're the bigger person.
☐ You still have your honor.
☐ You still have your hair.
☐ Heartbreak makes you wiser.
☐ People will see through that.
☐ You'll be the last one standing.
☐ Don't let it get you down.
☐ It's not forever.
☐ There are always people like that.
☐ Never fear, karma's a bitch.
☐ I think it looks cute.
☐ One door closes, another opens.
☐ It's all part of the plan.
☐ Go ahead, cry it out.
☐ They spelled your name right.
☐ Jobs come, jobs go.
☐ People come, people go.
☐ This must be hard for you.
☐ Time to get on with your life.
☐ Everyone's a critic.
☐ It's for the best.
☐ Don't go there.
☐ It's their loss.
☐ You can focus on your career.
☐ You can focus on your kids.
☐ Didn't kill ya; made ya stronger.
☐ Ours is not to reason why.
☐ Don't take it home with you.
☐ Timing is everything.
☐ You'll eventually love it.
☐ Think positive.
☐ Think denial.

☐ Someday you'll understand.
☐ Single life is actually better.
☐ Always darkest before the dawn.
☐ Just clear the browser history.
☐ You're still young.
☐ He isn't worth it.
☐ She isn't worth it.
☐ Where there's a will . . .
☐ Chalk it up to experience.
☐ Cross that bridge later.
☐ One day at a time.
☐ You can always get it fixed.
☐ Don't sweat the small stuff.
☐ Not over 'til the fat lady sings.
☐ It's all nonsense anyway.
☐ You gotta believe in you.
☐ I believe in you.
☐ Anything is possible.
☐ You reacted with integrity.
☐ You can sell it online.
☐ Don't get mad, get even.
☐ No one can tell it's a knockoff.
☐ Just say no.
☐ Hang in there, baby.
☐ If it's not one thing, it's another.
☐ It'll build character.
☐ It was meant to be.
☐ It wasn't meant to be.
☐ If it's meant to be, it'll happen.
☐ Keep your chin up.
☐ You don't need their approval.
☐ For every hill there's a valley.
☐ I would've done the same.
☐ Life goes on.
☐ Absence makes love stronger.
☐ Can't beat 'em? Join 'em.
☐ Shake it off.
☐ No one heard it.
☐ Better late than never.
☐ Better safe than sorry.
☐ And so it goes.
☐ The first cut is the deepest.
☐ Love hurts.
☐ Love stinks.
☐ Love is overrated.
☐ Soon this'll be a distant memory.
☐ Keep on truckin'.
☐ Quit worrying.
☐ It's water under the bridge.
☐ Don't dwell on it.

☐ Ya gotta do what ya gotta do.
☐ When it rains, it pours.
☐ Every rose has a thorn.
☐ You gave it your best shot.
☐ There, there.
☐ It takes all kinds.
☐ They're just jealous.
☐ It'll come when you're ready.
☐ Nobody mentioned it.
☐ Try to keep it in perspective.
☐ Put on your big girl panties.
☐ Put on your big boy briefs.
☐ There's a lid for every pot.
☐ He's probably out of town.
☐ Her phone is probably dead.
☐ You're better off.
☐ It happens sometimes.
☐ They don't understand you.
☐ It was an honest mistake.
☐ Money can't buy love.
☐ Adversity forges character.
☐ You'll feel better after a bath.
☐ You'll feel better after a drink.
☐ It'll make great memoir material.
☐ Quit blaming yourself.
☐ There's no such thing as normal.
☐ You'll show them.
☐ This will forge your character.
☐ You're a superstar.
☐ Just explain what happened.
☐ Don't compare.
☐ All parents screw up.
☐ All kids screw up.
☐ At least you have your health.
☐ He'll grow out of it.
☐ She'll grow out of it.
☐ Shhh. Shhh. It's okay now.
☐ Pain is temporary.
☐ I agree with you.
☐ One day you'll know why.
☐ You march to your own beat.
☐ Ignore what others think.
☐ Buck up, buckwheat.
☐ Everyone sympathizes.
☐ You're overthinking this.
☐ Get back up on the horse.
☐ Just give it some time.
☐ It's not the end of the world.
☐ It gets better.
☐ Really, it is.

☐ **TOTALLY OKAY** ☐ **PRETTY OKAY** ☐ **OKAY-ISH**

SIGNATURE MONTH DAY YEAR

"OKAY? OKAY. OKAY!"

IT'S GONNA BE OKAY

☐ **RIGHT NOW** ☐ **FAIRLY SOON** ☐ **EVENTUALLY**

☐ It'll grow back.
☐ You'll get over it.
☐ You can do this.
☐ It wasn't that obvious.
☐ This too shall pass.
☐ You're too good for him.
☐ You're too good for her.
☐ I'll never tell.
☐ Don't blame yourself.
☐ There are other fish in the sea.
☐ Tattoo removal is easier now.
☐ You are not your job.
☐ Your mother will never know.
☐ Nothing therapy won't cure.
☐ Just take a mulligan.
☐ Moving home is no big deal.
☐ Don't "should" all over yourself.
☐ At least you know you're right.
☐ You did your best.
☐ Can't win 'em all.
☐ You couldn't have known.
☐ My cousin had that and was fine.
☐ Laughter is the best medicine.
☐ Have faith.
☐ Penicillin clears that up fast.
☐ He wasn't thinking.
☐ She wasn't thinking.
☐ If at first you don't succeed . . .
☐ It's about quality, not quantity.
☐ That's not old, it's vintage.
☐ You're not old, you're vintage.
☐ Things happen for a reason.
☐ It'll look better in the morning.
☐ You can blog about it.
☐ We'll look back later and laugh.
☐ No one will ever know.
☐ Here's a hug.
☐ They don't deserve you.
☐ Every cloud has a silver lining.
☐ It was totally his fault.
☐ It was totally her fault.
☐ A rising tide lifts all boats.
☐ There are specialists for that.
☐ Think of the big picture.
☐ Don't let it bother you so much.
☐ No one saw you trip.
☐ You'll get that promotion soon.
☐ It could've been much worse.
☐ Aim for the stars.
☐ You'll forget about it, I promise.

☐ All publicity is good publicity.
☐ You can always return it.
☐ That was so understandable.
☐ You look great.
☐ You look great for your age.
☐ That happens to everyone.
☐ You made your point.
☐ Who wants that responsibility?
☐ It's not more than you can handle.
☐ Time heals all wounds.
☐ Time wounds all heels.
☐ I'm sure you don't normally do that.
☐ Success or not, you are loved.
☐ It's a journey, not a destination.
☐ It was a long shot anyway.
☐ Lesson learned.
☐ It's not you, it's the economy.
☐ You can always sue.
☐ You're the bigger person.
☐ You still have your honor.
☐ You still have your hair.
☐ Heartbreak makes you wiser.
☐ People will see through that.
☐ You'll be the last one standing.
☐ Don't let it get you down.
☐ It's not forever.
☐ There are always people like that.
☐ Never fear, karma's a bitch.
☐ I think it looks cute.
☐ One door closes, another opens.
☐ It's all part of the plan.
☐ Go ahead, cry it out.
☐ They spelled your name right.
☐ Jobs come, jobs go.
☐ People come, people go.
☐ This must be hard for you.
☐ Time to get on with your life.
☐ Everyone's a critic.
☐ It's for the best.
☐ Don't go there.
☐ It's their loss.
☐ You can focus on your career.
☐ You can focus on your kids.
☐ Didn't kill ya; made ya stronger.
☐ Ours is not to reason why.
☐ Don't take it home with you.
☐ Timing is everything.
☐ You'll eventually love it.
☐ Think positive.
☐ Think denial.

☐ Someday you'll understand.
☐ Single life is actually better.
☐ Always darkest before the dawn.
☐ Just clear the browser history.
☐ You're still young.
☐ He isn't worth it.
☐ She isn't worth it.
☐ Where there's a will . . .
☐ Chalk it up to experience.
☐ Cross that bridge later.
☐ One day at a time.
☐ You can always get it fixed.
☐ Don't sweat the small stuff.
☐ Not over 'til the fat lady sings.
☐ It's all nonsense anyway.
☐ You gotta believe in you.
☐ I believe in you.
☐ Anything is possible.
☐ You reacted with integrity.
☐ You can sell it online.
☐ Don't get mad, get even.
☐ No one can tell it's a knockoff.
☐ Just say no.
☐ Hang in there, baby.
☐ If it's not one thing, it's another.
☐ It'll build character.
☐ It was meant to be.
☐ It wasn't meant to be.
☐ If it's meant to be, it'll happen.
☐ Keep your chin up.
☐ You don't need their approval.
☐ For every hill there's a valley.
☐ I would've done the same.
☐ Life goes on.
☐ Absence makes love stronger.
☐ Can't beat 'em? Join 'em.
☐ Shake it off.
☐ No one heard it.
☐ Better late than never.
☐ Better safe than sorry.
☐ And so it goes.
☐ The first cut is the deepest.
☐ Love hurts.
☐ Love stinks.
☐ Love is overrated.
☐ Soon this'll be a distant memory.
☐ Keep on truckin'.
☐ Quit worrying.
☐ It's water under the bridge.
☐ Don't dwell on it.

☐ Ya gotta do what ya gotta do.
☐ When it rains, it pours.
☐ Every rose has a thorn.
☐ You gave it your best shot.
☐ There, there.
☐ It takes all kinds.
☐ They're just jealous.
☐ It'll come when you're ready.
☐ Nobody mentioned it.
☐ Try to keep it in perspective.
☐ Put on your big girl panties.
☐ Put on your big boy briefs.
☐ There's a lid for every pot.
☐ He's probably out of town.
☐ Her phone is probably dead.
☐ You're better off.
☐ It happens sometimes.
☐ They don't understand you.
☐ It was an honest mistake.
☐ Money can't buy love.
☐ Adversity forges character.
☐ You'll feel better after a bath.
☐ You'll feel better after a drink.
☐ It'll make great memoir material.
☐ Quit blaming yourself.
☐ There's no such thing as normal.
☐ You'll show them.
☐ This will forge your character.
☐ You're a superstar.
☐ Just explain what happened.
☐ Don't compare.
☐ All parents screw up.
☐ All kids screw up.
☐ At least you have your health.
☐ He'll grow out of it.
☐ She'll grow out of it.
☐ Shhh. Shhh. It's okay now.
☐ Pain is temporary.
☐ I agree with you.
☐ One day you'll know why.
☐ You march to your own beat.
☐ Ignore what others think.
☐ Buck up, buckwheat.
☐ Everyone sympathizes.
☐ You're overthinking this.
☐ Get back up on the horse.
☐ Just give it some time.
☐ It's not the end of the world.
☐ It gets better.
☐ Really, it is.

☐ **TOTALLY OKAY** ☐ **PRETTY OKAY** ☐ **OKAY-ISH**

SIGNATURE MONTH DAY YEAR

"OKAY? OKAY. OKAY!"

IT'S GONNA BE OKAY

☐ RIGHT NOW ☐ FAIRLY SOON ☐ EVENTUALLY

☐ It'll grow back.
☐ You'll get over it.
☐ You can do this.
☐ It wasn't that obvious.
☐ This too shall pass.
☐ You're too good for him.
☐ You're too good for her.
☐ I'll never tell.
☐ Don't blame yourself.
☐ There are other fish in the sea.
☐ Tattoo removal is easier now.
☐ You are not your job.
☐ Your mother will never know.
☐ Nothing therapy won't cure.
☐ Just take a mulligan.
☐ Moving home is no big deal.
☐ Don't "should" all over yourself.
☐ At least you know you're right.
☐ You did your best.
☐ Can't win 'em all.
☐ You couldn't have known.
☐ My cousin had that and was fine.
☐ Laughter is the best medicine.
☐ Have faith.
☐ Penicillin clears that up fast.
☐ He wasn't thinking.
☐ She wasn't thinking.
☐ If at first you don't succeed . . .
☐ It's about quality, not quantity.
☐ That's not old, it's vintage.
☐ You're not old, you're vintage.
☐ Things happen for a reason.
☐ It'll look better in the morning.
☐ You can blog about it.
☐ We'll look back later and laugh.
☐ No one will ever know.
☐ Here's a hug.
☐ They don't deserve you.
☐ Every cloud has a silver lining.
☐ It was totally his fault.
☐ It was totally her fault.
☐ A rising tide lifts all boats.
☐ There are specialists for that.
☐ Think of the big picture.
☐ Don't let it bother you so much.
☐ No one saw you trip.
☐ You'll get that promotion soon.
☐ It could've been much worse.
☐ Aim for the stars.
☐ You'll forget about it, I promise.

☐ All publicity is good publicity.
☐ You can always return it.
☐ That was so understandable.
☐ You look great.
☐ You look great for your age.
☐ That happens to everyone.
☐ You made your point.
☐ Who wants that responsibility?
☐ It's not more than you can handle.
☐ Time heals all wounds.
☐ Time wounds all heels.
☐ I'm sure you don't normally do that.
☐ Success or not, you are loved.
☐ It's a journey, not a destination.
☐ It was a long shot anyway.
☐ Lesson learned.
☐ It's not you, it's the economy.
☐ You can always sue.
☐ You're the bigger person.
☐ You still have your honor.
☐ You still have your hair.
☐ Heartbreak makes you wiser.
☐ People will see through that.
☐ You'll be the last one standing.
☐ Don't let it get you down.
☐ It's not forever.
☐ There are always people like that.
☐ Never fear, karma's a bitch.
☐ I think it looks cute.
☐ One door closes, another opens.
☐ It's all part of the plan.
☐ Go ahead, cry it out.
☐ They spelled your name right.
☐ Jobs come, jobs go.
☐ People come, people go.
☐ This must be hard for you.
☐ Time to get on with your life.
☐ Everyone's a critic.
☐ It's for the best.
☐ Don't go there.
☐ It's their loss.
☐ You can focus on your career.
☐ You can focus on your kids.
☐ Didn't kill ya; made ya stronger.
☐ Ours is not to reason why.
☐ Don't take it home with you.
☐ Timing is everything.
☐ You'll eventually love it.
☐ Think positive.
☐ Think denial.

☐ Someday you'll understand.
☐ Single life is actually better.
☐ Always darkest before the dawn.
☐ Just clear the browser history.
☐ You're still young.
☐ He isn't worth it.
☐ She isn't worth it.
☐ Where there's a will . . .
☐ Chalk it up to experience.
☐ Cross that bridge later.
☐ One day at a time.
☐ You can always get it fixed.
☐ Don't sweat the small stuff.
☐ Not over 'til the fat lady sings.
☐ It's all nonsense anyway.
☐ You gotta believe in you.
☐ I believe in you.
☐ Anything is possible.
☐ You reacted with integrity.
☐ You can sell it online.
☐ Don't get mad, get even.
☐ No one can tell it's a knockoff.
☐ Just say no.
☐ Hang in there, baby.
☐ If it's not one thing, it's another.
☐ It'll build character.
☐ It was meant to be.
☐ It wasn't meant to be.
☐ If it's meant to be, it'll happen.
☐ Keep your chin up.
☐ You don't need their approval.
☐ For every hill there's a valley.
☐ I would've done the same.
☐ Life goes on.
☐ Absence makes love stronger.
☐ Can't beat 'em? Join 'em.
☐ Shake it off.
☐ No one heard it.
☐ Better late than never.
☐ Better safe than sorry.
☐ And so it goes.
☐ The first cut is the deepest.
☐ Love hurts.
☐ Love stinks.
☐ Love is overrated.
☐ Soon this'll be a distant memory.
☐ Keep on truckin'.
☐ Quit worrying.
☐ It's water under the bridge.
☐ Don't dwell on it.

☐ Ya gotta do what ya gotta do.
☐ When it rains, it pours.
☐ Every rose has a thorn.
☐ You gave it your best shot.
☐ There, there.
☐ It takes all kinds.
☐ They're just jealous.
☐ It'll come when you're ready.
☐ Nobody mentioned it.
☐ Try to keep it in perspective.
☐ Put on your big girl panties.
☐ Put on your big boy briefs.
☐ There's a lid for every pot.
☐ He's probably out of town.
☐ Her phone is probably dead.
☐ You're better off.
☐ It happens sometimes.
☐ They don't understand you.
☐ It was an honest mistake.
☐ Money can't buy love.
☐ Adversity forges character.
☐ You'll feel better after a bath.
☐ You'll feel better after a drink.
☐ It'll make great memoir material.
☐ Quit blaming yourself.
☐ There's no such thing as normal.
☐ You'll show them.
☐ This will forge your character.
☐ You're a superstar.
☐ Just explain what happened.
☐ Don't compare.
☐ All parents screw up.
☐ All kids screw up.
☐ At least you have your health.
☐ He'll grow out of it.
☐ She'll grow out of it.
☐ Shhh. Shhh. It's okay now.
☐ Pain is temporary.
☐ I agree with you.
☐ One day you'll know why.
☐ You march to your own beat.
☐ Ignore what others think.
☐ Buck up, buckwheat.
☐ Everyone sympathizes.
☐ You're overthinking this.
☐ Get back up on the horse.
☐ Just give it some time.
☐ It's not the end of the world.
☐ It gets better.
☐ Really, it is.

☐ TOTALLY OKAY ☐ PRETTY OKAY ☐ OKAY-ISH

SIGNATURE

MONTH : DAY : YEAR

"OKAY? OKAY. OKAY!"

IT'S GONNA BE OKAY

☐ **RIGHT NOW** ☐ **FAIRLY SOON** ☐ **EVENTUALLY**

- ☐ It'll grow back.
- ☐ You'll get over it.
- ☐ You can do this.
- ☐ It wasn't that obvious.
- ☐ This too shall pass.
- ☐ You're too good for him.
- ☐ You're too good for her.
- ☐ I'll never tell.
- ☐ Don't blame yourself.
- ☐ There are other fish in the sea.
- ☐ Tattoo removal is easier now.
- ☐ You are not your job.
- ☐ Your mother will never know.
- ☐ Nothing therapy won't cure.
- ☐ Just take a mulligan.
- ☐ Moving home is no big deal.
- ☐ Don't "should" all over yourself.
- ☐ At least you know you're right.
- ☐ You did your best.
- ☐ Can't win 'em all.
- ☐ You couldn't have known.
- ☐ My cousin had that and was fine.
- ☐ Laughter is the best medicine.
- ☐ Have faith.
- ☐ Penicillin clears that up fast.
- ☐ He wasn't thinking.
- ☐ She wasn't thinking.
- ☐ If at first you don't succeed . . .
- ☐ It's about quality, not quantity.
- ☐ That's not old, it's vintage.
- ☐ You're not old, you're vintage.
- ☐ Things happen for a reason.
- ☐ It'll look better in the morning.
- ☐ You can blog about it.
- ☐ We'll look back later and laugh.
- ☐ No one will ever know.
- ☐ Here's a hug.
- ☐ They don't deserve you.
- ☐ Every cloud has a silver lining.
- ☐ It was totally his fault.
- ☐ It was totally her fault.
- ☐ A rising tide lifts all boats.
- ☐ There are specialists for that.
- ☐ Think of the big picture.
- ☐ Don't let it bother you so much.
- ☐ No one saw you trip.
- ☐ You'll get that promotion soon.
- ☐ It could've been much worse.
- ☐ Aim for the stars.
- ☐ You'll forget about it, I promise.
- ☐ All publicity is good publicity.
- ☐ You can always return it.
- ☐ That was so understandable.
- ☐ You look great.
- ☐ You look great for your age.
- ☐ That happens to everyone.
- ☐ You made your point.
- ☐ Who wants that responsibility?
- ☐ It's not more than you can handle.
- ☐ Time heals all wounds.
- ☐ Time wounds all heels.
- ☐ I'm sure you don't normally do that.
- ☐ Success or not, you are loved.
- ☐ It's a journey, not a destination.
- ☐ It was a long shot anyway.
- ☐ Lesson learned.
- ☐ It's not you, it's the economy.
- ☐ You can always sue.
- ☐ You're the bigger person.
- ☐ You still have your honor.
- ☐ You still have your hair.
- ☐ Heartbreak makes you wiser.
- ☐ People will see through that.
- ☐ You'll be the last one standing.
- ☐ Don't let it get you down.
- ☐ It's not forever.
- ☐ There are always people like that.
- ☐ Never fear, karma's a bitch.
- ☐ I think it looks cute.
- ☐ One door closes, another opens.
- ☐ It's all part of the plan.
- ☐ Go ahead, cry it out.
- ☐ They spelled your name right.
- ☐ Jobs come, jobs go.
- ☐ People come, people go.
- ☐ This must be hard for you.
- ☐ Time to get on with your life.
- ☐ Everyone's a critic.
- ☐ It's for the best.
- ☐ Don't go there.
- ☐ It's their loss.
- ☐ You can focus on your career.
- ☐ You can focus on your kids.
- ☐ Didn't kill ya; made ya stronger.
- ☐ Ours is not to reason why.
- ☐ Don't take it home with you.
- ☐ Timing is everything.
- ☐ You'll eventually love it.
- ☐ Think positive.
- ☐ Think denial.
- ☐ Someday you'll understand.
- ☐ Single life is actually better.
- ☐ Always darkest before the dawn.
- ☐ Just clear the browser history.
- ☐ You're still young.
- ☐ He isn't worth it.
- ☐ She isn't worth it.
- ☐ Where there's a will . . .
- ☐ Chalk it up to experience.
- ☐ Cross that bridge later.
- ☐ One day at a time.
- ☐ You can always get it fixed.
- ☐ Don't sweat the small stuff.
- ☐ Not over 'til the fat lady sings.
- ☐ It's all nonsense anyway.
- ☐ You gotta believe in you.
- ☐ I believe in you.
- ☐ Anything is possible.
- ☐ You reacted with integrity.
- ☐ You can sell it online.
- ☐ Don't get mad, get even.
- ☐ No one can tell it's a knockoff.
- ☐ Just say no.
- ☐ Hang in there, baby.
- ☐ If it's not one thing, it's another.
- ☐ It'll build character.
- ☐ It was meant to be.
- ☐ It wasn't meant to be.
- ☐ If it's meant to be, it'll happen.
- ☐ Keep your chin up.
- ☐ You don't need their approval.
- ☐ For every hill there's a valley.
- ☐ I would've done the same.
- ☐ Life goes on.
- ☐ Absence makes love stronger.
- ☐ Can't beat 'em? Join 'em.
- ☐ Shake it off.
- ☐ No one heard it.
- ☐ Better late than never.
- ☐ Better safe than sorry.
- ☐ And so it goes.
- ☐ The first cut is the deepest.
- ☐ Love hurts.
- ☐ Love stinks.
- ☐ Love is overrated.
- ☐ Soon this'll be a distant memory.
- ☐ Keep on truckin'.
- ☐ Quit worrying.
- ☐ It's water under the bridge.
- ☐ Don't dwell on it.
- ☐ Ya gotta do what ya gotta do.
- ☐ When it rains, it pours.
- ☐ Every rose has a thorn.
- ☐ You gave it your best shot.
- ☐ There, there.
- ☐ It takes all kinds.
- ☐ They're just jealous.
- ☐ It'll come when you're ready.
- ☐ Nobody mentioned it.
- ☐ Try to keep it in perspective.
- ☐ Put on your big girl panties.
- ☐ Put on your big boy briefs.
- ☐ There's a lid for every pot.
- ☐ He's probably out of town.
- ☐ Her phone is probably dead.
- ☐ You're better off.
- ☐ It happens sometimes.
- ☐ They don't understand you.
- ☐ It was an honest mistake.
- ☐ Money can't buy love.
- ☐ Adversity forges character.
- ☐ You'll feel better after a bath.
- ☐ You'll feel better after a drink.
- ☐ It'll make great memoir material.
- ☐ Quit blaming yourself.
- ☐ There's no such thing as normal.
- ☐ You'll show them.
- ☐ This will forge your character.
- ☐ You're a superstar.
- ☐ Just explain what happened.
- ☐ Don't compare.
- ☐ All parents screw up.
- ☐ All kids screw up.
- ☐ At least you have your health.
- ☐ He'll grow out of it.
- ☐ She'll grow out of it.
- ☐ Shhh. Shhh. It's okay now.
- ☐ Pain is temporary.
- ☐ I agree with you.
- ☐ One day you'll know why.
- ☐ You march to your own beat.
- ☐ Ignore what others think.
- ☐ Buck up, buckwheat.
- ☐ Everyone sympathizes.
- ☐ You're overthinking this.
- ☐ Get back up on the horse.
- ☐ Just give it some time.
- ☐ It's not the end of the world.
- ☐ It gets better.
- ☐ Really, it is.

☐ **TOTALLY OKAY** ☐ **PRETTY OKAY** ☐ **OKAY-ISH**

SIGNATURE	MONTH	DAY	YEAR

"OKAY? OKAY. OKAY!"

IT'S GONNA BE OKAY

☐ **RIGHT NOW** ☐ **FAIRLY SOON** ☐ **EVENTUALLY**

- ☐ It'll grow back.
- ☐ You'll get over it.
- ☐ You can do this.
- ☐ It wasn't that obvious.
- ☐ This too shall pass.
- ☐ You're too good for him.
- ☐ You're too good for her.
- ☐ I'll never tell.
- ☐ Don't blame yourself.
- ☐ There are other fish in the sea.
- ☐ Tattoo removal is easier now.
- ☐ You are not your job.
- ☐ Your mother will never know.
- ☐ Nothing therapy won't cure.
- ☐ Just take a mulligan.
- ☐ Moving home is no big deal.
- ☐ Don't "should" all over yourself.
- ☐ At least you know you're right.
- ☐ You did your best.
- ☐ Can't win 'em all.
- ☐ You couldn't have known.
- ☐ My cousin had that and was fine.
- ☐ Laughter is the best medicine.
- ☐ Have faith.
- ☐ Penicillin clears that up fast.
- ☐ He wasn't thinking.
- ☐ She wasn't thinking.
- ☐ If at first you don't succeed . . .
- ☐ It's about quality, not quantity.
- ☐ That's not old, it's vintage.
- ☐ You're not old, you're vintage.
- ☐ Things happen for a reason.
- ☐ It'll look better in the morning.
- ☐ You can blog about it.
- ☐ We'll look back later and laugh.
- ☐ No one will ever know.
- ☐ Here's a hug.
- ☐ They don't deserve you.
- ☐ Every cloud has a silver lining.
- ☐ It was totally his fault.
- ☐ It was totally her fault.
- ☐ A rising tide lifts all boats.
- ☐ There are specialists for that.
- ☐ Think of the big picture.
- ☐ Don't let it bother you so much.
- ☐ No one saw you trip.
- ☐ You'll get that promotion soon.
- ☐ It could've been much worse.
- ☐ Aim for the stars.
- ☐ You'll forget about it, I promise.
- ☐ All publicity is good publicity.
- ☐ You can always return it.
- ☐ That was so understandable.
- ☐ You look great.
- ☐ You look great for your age.
- ☐ That happens to everyone.
- ☐ You made your point.
- ☐ Who wants that responsibility?
- ☐ It's not more than you can handle.
- ☐ Time heals all wounds.
- ☐ Time wounds all heels.
- ☐ I'm sure you don't normally do that.
- ☐ Success or not, you are loved.
- ☐ It's a journey, not a destination.
- ☐ It was a long shot anyway.
- ☐ Lesson learned.
- ☐ It's not you, it's the economy.
- ☐ You can always sue.
- ☐ You're the bigger person.
- ☐ You still have your honor.
- ☐ You still have your hair.
- ☐ Heartbreak makes you wiser.
- ☐ People will see through that.
- ☐ You'll be the last one standing.
- ☐ Don't let it get you down.
- ☐ It's not forever.
- ☐ There are always people like that.
- ☐ Never fear, karma's a bitch.
- ☐ I think it looks cute.
- ☐ One door closes, another opens.
- ☐ It's all part of the plan.
- ☐ Go ahead, cry it out.
- ☐ They spelled your name right.
- ☐ Jobs come, jobs go.
- ☐ People come, people go.
- ☐ This must be hard for you.
- ☐ Time to get on with your life.
- ☐ Everyone's a critic.
- ☐ It's for the best.
- ☐ Don't go there.
- ☐ It's their loss.
- ☐ You can focus on your career.
- ☐ You can focus on your kids.
- ☐ Didn't kill ya; made ya stronger.
- ☐ Ours is not to reason why.
- ☐ Don't take it home with you.
- ☐ Timing is everything.
- ☐ You'll eventually love it.
- ☐ Think positive.
- ☐ Think denial.
- ☐ Someday you'll understand.
- ☐ Single life is actually better.
- ☐ Always darkest before the dawn.
- ☐ Just clear the browser history.
- ☐ You're still young.
- ☐ He isn't worth it.
- ☐ She isn't worth it.
- ☐ Where there's a will . . .
- ☐ Chalk it up to experience.
- ☐ Cross that bridge later.
- ☐ One day at a time.
- ☐ You can always get it fixed.
- ☐ Don't sweat the small stuff.
- ☐ Not over 'til the fat lady sings.
- ☐ It's all nonsense anyway.
- ☐ You gotta believe in you.
- ☐ I believe in you.
- ☐ Anything is possible.
- ☐ You reacted with integrity.
- ☐ You can sell it online.
- ☐ Don't get mad, get even.
- ☐ No one can tell it's a knockoff.
- ☐ Just say no.
- ☐ Hang in there, baby.
- ☐ If it's not one thing, it's another.
- ☐ It'll build character.
- ☐ It was meant to be.
- ☐ It wasn't meant to be.
- ☐ If it's meant to be, it'll happen.
- ☐ Keep your chin up.
- ☐ You don't need their approval.
- ☐ For every hill there's a valley.
- ☐ I would've done the same.
- ☐ Life goes on.
- ☐ Absence makes love stronger.
- ☐ Can't beat 'em? Join 'em.
- ☐ Shake it off.
- ☐ No one heard it.
- ☐ Better late than never.
- ☐ Better safe than sorry.
- ☐ And so it goes.
- ☐ The first cut is the deepest.
- ☐ Love hurts.
- ☐ Love stinks.
- ☐ Love is overrated.
- ☐ Soon this'll be a distant memory.
- ☐ Keep on truckin'.
- ☐ Quit worrying.
- ☐ It's water under the bridge.
- ☐ Don't dwell on it.
- ☐ Ya gotta do what ya gotta do.
- ☐ When it rains, it pours.
- ☐ Every rose has a thorn.
- ☐ You gave it your best shot.
- ☐ There, there.
- ☐ It takes all kinds.
- ☐ They're just jealous.
- ☐ It'll come when you're ready.
- ☐ Nobody mentioned it.
- ☐ Try to keep it in perspective.
- ☐ Put on your big girl panties.
- ☐ Put on your big boy briefs.
- ☐ There's a lid for every pot.
- ☐ He's probably out of town.
- ☐ Her phone is probably dead.
- ☐ You're better off.
- ☐ It happens sometimes.
- ☐ They don't understand you.
- ☐ It was an honest mistake.
- ☐ Money can't buy love.
- ☐ Adversity forges character.
- ☐ You'll feel better after a bath.
- ☐ You'll feel better after a drink.
- ☐ It'll make great memoir material.
- ☐ Quit blaming yourself.
- ☐ There's no such thing as normal.
- ☐ You'll show them.
- ☐ This will forge your character.
- ☐ You're a superstar.
- ☐ Just explain what happened.
- ☐ Don't compare.
- ☐ All parents screw up.
- ☐ All kids screw up.
- ☐ At least you have your health.
- ☐ He'll grow out of it.
- ☐ She'll grow out of it.
- ☐ Shhh. Shhh. It's okay now.
- ☐ Pain is temporary.
- ☐ I agree with you.
- ☐ One day you'll know why.
- ☐ You march to your own beat.
- ☐ Ignore what others think.
- ☐ Buck up, buckwheat.
- ☐ Everyone sympathizes.
- ☐ You're overthinking this.
- ☐ Get back up on the horse.
- ☐ Just give it some time.
- ☐ It's not the end of the world.
- ☐ It gets better.
- ☐ Really, it is.

☐ **TOTALLY OKAY** ☐ **PRETTY OKAY** ☐ **OKAY-ISH**

SIGNATURE	MONTH	DAY	YEAR

"OKAY? OKAY. OKAY!"

IT'S GONNA BE OKAY

☐ **RIGHT NOW** ☐ **FAIRLY SOON** ☐ **EVENTUALLY**

- ☐ It'll grow back.
- ☐ You'll get over it.
- ☐ You can do this.
- ☐ It wasn't that obvious.
- ☐ This too shall pass.
- ☐ You're too good for him.
- ☐ You're too good for her.
- ☐ I'll never tell.
- ☐ Don't blame yourself.
- ☐ There are other fish in the sea.
- ☐ Tattoo removal is easier now.
- ☐ You are not your job.
- ☐ Your mother will never know.
- ☐ Nothing therapy won't cure.
- ☐ Just take a mulligan.
- ☐ Moving home is no big deal.
- ☐ Don't "should" all over yourself.
- ☐ At least you know you're right.
- ☐ You did your best.
- ☐ Can't win 'em all.
- ☐ You couldn't have known.
- ☐ My cousin had that and was fine.
- ☐ Laughter is the best medicine.
- ☐ Have faith.
- ☐ Penicillin clears that up fast.
- ☐ He wasn't thinking.
- ☐ She wasn't thinking.
- ☐ If at first you don't succeed . . .
- ☐ It's about quality, not quantity.
- ☐ That's not old, it's vintage.
- ☐ You're not old, you're vintage.
- ☐ Things happen for a reason.
- ☐ It'll look better in the morning.
- ☐ You can blog about it.
- ☐ We'll look back later and laugh.
- ☐ No one will ever know.
- ☐ Here's a hug.
- ☐ They don't deserve you.
- ☐ Every cloud has a silver lining.
- ☐ It was totally his fault.
- ☐ It was totally her fault.
- ☐ A rising tide lifts all boats.
- ☐ There are specialists for that.
- ☐ Think of the big picture.
- ☐ Don't let it bother you so much.
- ☐ No one saw you trip.
- ☐ You'll get that promotion soon.
- ☐ It could've been much worse.
- ☐ Aim for the stars.
- ☐ You'll forget about it, I promise.
- ☐ All publicity is good publicity.
- ☐ You can always return it.
- ☐ That was so understandable.
- ☐ You look great.
- ☐ You look great for your age.
- ☐ That happens to everyone.
- ☐ You made your point.
- ☐ Who wants that responsibility?
- ☐ It's not more than you can handle.
- ☐ Time heals all wounds.
- ☐ Time wounds all heels.
- ☐ I'm sure you don't normally do that.
- ☐ Success or not, you are loved.
- ☐ It's a journey, not a destination.
- ☐ It was a long shot anyway.
- ☐ Lesson learned.
- ☐ It's not you, it's the economy.
- ☐ You can always sue.
- ☐ You're the bigger person.
- ☐ You still have your honor.
- ☐ You still have your hair.
- ☐ Heartbreak makes you wiser.
- ☐ People will see through that.
- ☐ You'll be the last one standing.
- ☐ Don't let it get you down.
- ☐ It's not forever.
- ☐ There are always people like that.
- ☐ Never fear, karma's a bitch.
- ☐ I think it looks cute.
- ☐ One door closes, another opens.
- ☐ It's all part of the plan.
- ☐ Go ahead, cry it out.
- ☐ They spelled your name right.
- ☐ Jobs come, jobs go.
- ☐ People come, people go.
- ☐ This must be hard for you.
- ☐ Time to get on with your life.
- ☐ Everyone's a critic.
- ☐ It's for the best.
- ☐ Don't go there.
- ☐ It's their loss.
- ☐ You can focus on your career.
- ☐ You can focus on your kids.
- ☐ Didn't kill ya; made ya stronger.
- ☐ Ours is not to reason why.
- ☐ Don't take it home with you.
- ☐ Timing is everything.
- ☐ You'll eventually love it.
- ☐ Think positive.
- ☐ Think denial.
- ☐ Someday you'll understand.
- ☐ Single life is actually better.
- ☐ Always darkest before the dawn.
- ☐ Just clear the browser history.
- ☐ You're still young.
- ☐ He isn't worth it.
- ☐ She isn't worth it.
- ☐ Where there's a will . . .
- ☐ Chalk it up to experience.
- ☐ Cross that bridge later.
- ☐ One day at a time.
- ☐ You can always get it fixed.
- ☐ Don't sweat the small stuff.
- ☐ Not over 'til the fat lady sings.
- ☐ It's all nonsense anyway.
- ☐ You gotta believe in you.
- ☐ I believe in you.
- ☐ Anything is possible.
- ☐ You reacted with integrity.
- ☐ You can sell it online.
- ☐ Don't get mad, get even.
- ☐ No one can tell it's a knockoff.
- ☐ Just say no.
- ☐ Hang in there, baby.
- ☐ If it's not one thing, it's another.
- ☐ It'll build character.
- ☐ It was meant to be.
- ☐ It wasn't meant to be.
- ☐ If it's meant to be, it'll happen.
- ☐ Keep your chin up.
- ☐ You don't need their approval.
- ☐ For every hill there's a valley.
- ☐ I would've done the same.
- ☐ Life goes on.
- ☐ Absence makes love stronger.
- ☐ Can't beat 'em? Join 'em.
- ☐ Shake it off.
- ☐ No one heard it.
- ☐ Better late than never.
- ☐ Better safe than sorry.
- ☐ And so it goes.
- ☐ The first cut is the deepest.
- ☐ Love hurts.
- ☐ Love stinks.
- ☐ Love is overrated.
- ☐ Soon this'll be a distant memory.
- ☐ Keep on truckin'.
- ☐ Quit worrying.
- ☐ It's water under the bridge.
- ☐ Don't dwell on it.
- ☐ Ya gotta do what ya gotta do.
- ☐ When it rains, it pours.
- ☐ Every rose has a thorn.
- ☐ You gave it your best shot.
- ☐ There, there.
- ☐ It takes all kinds.
- ☐ They're just jealous.
- ☐ It'll come when you're ready.
- ☐ Nobody mentioned it.
- ☐ Try to keep it in perspective.
- ☐ Put on your big girl panties.
- ☐ Put on your big boy briefs.
- ☐ There's a lid for every pot.
- ☐ He's probably out of town.
- ☐ Her phone is probably dead.
- ☐ You're better off.
- ☐ It happens sometimes.
- ☐ They don't understand you.
- ☐ It was an honest mistake.
- ☐ Money can't buy love.
- ☐ Adversity forges character.
- ☐ You'll feel better after a bath.
- ☐ You'll feel better after a drink.
- ☐ It'll make great memoir material.
- ☐ Quit blaming yourself.
- ☐ There's no such thing as normal.
- ☐ You'll show them.
- ☐ This will forge your character.
- ☐ You're a superstar.
- ☐ Just explain what happened.
- ☐ Don't compare.
- ☐ All parents screw up.
- ☐ All kids screw up.
- ☐ At least you have your health.
- ☐ He'll grow out of it.
- ☐ She'll grow out of it.
- ☐ Shhh. Shhh. It's okay now.
- ☐ Pain is temporary.
- ☐ I agree with you.
- ☐ One day you'll know why.
- ☐ You march to your own beat.
- ☐ Ignore what others think.
- ☐ Buck up, buckwheat.
- ☐ Everyone sympathizes.
- ☐ You're overthinking this.
- ☐ Get back up on the horse.
- ☐ Just give it some time.
- ☐ It's not the end of the world.
- ☐ It gets better.
- ☐ Really, it is.

☐ **TOTALLY OKAY** ☐ **PRETTY OKAY** ☐ **OKAY-ISH**

SIGNATURE

MONTH DAY YEAR

"OKAY? OKAY. OKAY!"

IT'S GONNA BE OKAY

☐ RIGHT NOW ☐ FAIRLY SOON ☐ EVENTUALLY

☐ It'll grow back.
☐ You'll get over it.
☐ You can do this.
☐ It wasn't that obvious.
☐ This too shall pass.
☐ You're too good for him.
☐ You're too good for her.
☐ I'll never tell.
☐ Don't blame yourself.
☐ There are other fish in the sea.
☐ Tattoo removal is easier now.
☐ You are not your job.
☐ Your mother will never know.
☐ Nothing therapy won't cure.
☐ Just take a mulligan.
☐ Moving home is no big deal.
☐ Don't "should" all over yourself.
☐ At least you know you're right.
☐ You did your best.
☐ Can't win 'em all.
☐ You couldn't have known.
☐ My cousin had that and was fine.
☐ Laughter is the best medicine.
☐ Have faith.
☐ Penicillin clears that up fast.
☐ He wasn't thinking.
☐ She wasn't thinking.
☐ If at first you don't succeed . . .
☐ It's about quality, not quantity.
☐ That's not old, it's vintage.
☐ You're not old, you're vintage.
☐ Things happen for a reason.
☐ It'll look better in the morning.
☐ You can blog about it.
☐ We'll look back later and laugh.
☐ No one will ever know.
☐ Here's a hug.
☐ They don't deserve you.
☐ Every cloud has a silver lining.
☐ It was totally his fault.
☐ It was totally her fault.
☐ A rising tide lifts all boats.
☐ There are specialists for that.
☐ Think of the big picture.
☐ Don't let it bother you so much.
☐ No one saw you trip.
☐ You'll get that promotion soon.
☐ It could've been much worse.
☐ Aim for the stars.
☐ You'll forget about it, I promise.

☐ All publicity is good publicity.
☐ You can always return it.
☐ That was so understandable.
☐ You look great.
☐ You look great for your age.
☐ That happens to everyone.
☐ You made your point.
☐ Who wants that responsibility?
☐ It's not more than you can handle.
☐ Time heals all wounds.
☐ Time wounds all heels.
☐ I'm sure you don't normally do that.
☐ Success or not, you are loved.
☐ It's a journey, not a destination.
☐ It was a long shot anyway.
☐ Lesson learned.
☐ It's not you, it's the economy.
☐ You can always sue.
☐ You're the bigger person.
☐ You still have your honor.
☐ You still have your hair.
☐ Heartbreak makes you wiser.
☐ People will see through that.
☐ You'll be the last one standing.
☐ Don't let it get you down.
☐ It's not forever.
☐ There are always people like that.
☐ Never fear, karma's a bitch.
☐ I think it looks cute.
☐ One door closes, another opens.
☐ It's all part of the plan.
☐ Go ahead, cry it out.
☐ They spelled your name right.
☐ Jobs come, jobs go.
☐ People come, people go.
☐ This must be hard for you.
☐ Time to get on with your life.
☐ Everyone's a critic.
☐ It's for the best.
☐ Don't go there.
☐ It's their loss.
☐ You can focus on your career.
☐ You can focus on your kids.
☐ Didn't kill ya; made ya stronger.
☐ Ours is not to reason why.
☐ Don't take it home with you.
☐ Timing is everything.
☐ You'll eventually love it.
☐ Think positive.
☐ Think denial.

☐ Someday you'll understand.
☐ Single life is actually better.
☐ Always darkest before the dawn.
☐ Just clear the browser history.
☐ You're still young.
☐ He isn't worth it.
☐ She isn't worth it.
☐ Where there's a will . . .
☐ Chalk it up to experience.
☐ Cross that bridge later.
☐ One day at a time.
☐ You can always get it fixed.
☐ Don't sweat the small stuff.
☐ Not over 'til the fat lady sings.
☐ It's all nonsense anyway.
☐ You gotta believe in you.
☐ I believe in you.
☐ Anything is possible.
☐ You reacted with integrity.
☐ You can sell it online.
☐ Don't get mad, get even.
☐ No one can tell it's a knockoff.
☐ Just say no.
☐ Hang in there, baby.
☐ If it's not one thing, it's another.
☐ It'll build character.
☐ It was meant to be.
☐ It wasn't meant to be.
☐ If it's meant to be, it'll happen.
☐ Keep your chin up.
☐ You don't need their approval.
☐ For every hill there's a valley.
☐ I would've done the same.
☐ Life goes on.
☐ Absence makes love stronger.
☐ Can't beat 'em? Join 'em.
☐ Shake it off.
☐ No one heard it.
☐ Better late than never.
☐ Better safe than sorry.
☐ And so it goes.
☐ The first cut is the deepest.
☐ Love hurts.
☐ Love stinks.
☐ Love is overrated.
☐ Soon this'll be a distant memory.
☐ Keep on truckin'.
☐ Quit worrying.
☐ It's water under the bridge.
☐ Don't dwell on it.

☐ Ya gotta do what ya gotta do.
☐ When it rains, it pours.
☐ Every rose has a thorn.
☐ You gave it your best shot.
☐ There, there.
☐ It takes all kinds.
☐ They're just jealous.
☐ It'll come when you're ready.
☐ Nobody mentioned it.
☐ Try to keep it in perspective.
☐ Put on your big girl panties.
☐ Put on your big boy briefs.
☐ There's a lid for every pot.
☐ He's probably out of town.
☐ Her phone is probably dead.
☐ You're better off.
☐ It happens sometimes.
☐ They don't understand you.
☐ It was an honest mistake.
☐ Money can't buy love.
☐ Adversity forges character.
☐ You'll feel better after a bath.
☐ You'll feel better after a drink.
☐ It'll make great memoir material.
☐ Quit blaming yourself.
☐ There's no such thing as normal.
☐ You'll show them.
☐ This will forge your character.
☐ You're a superstar.
☐ Just explain what happened.
☐ Don't compare.
☐ All parents screw up.
☐ All kids screw up.
☐ At least you have your health.
☐ He'll grow out of it.
☐ She'll grow out of it.
☐ Shhh. Shhh. It's okay now.
☐ Pain is temporary.
☐ I agree with you.
☐ One day you'll know why.
☐ You march to your own beat.
☐ Ignore what others think.
☐ Buck up, buckwheat.
☐ Everyone sympathizes.
☐ You're overthinking this.
☐ Get back up on the horse.
☐ Just give it some time.
☐ It's not the end of the world.
☐ It gets better.
☐ Really, it is.

☐ TOTALLY OKAY ☐ PRETTY OKAY ☐ OKAY-ISH

SIGNATURE

MONTH DAY YEAR

"OKAY? OKAY. OKAY!"

IT'S GONNA BE OKAY

☐ RIGHT NOW ☐ FAIRLY SOON ☐ EVENTUALLY

☐ It'll grow back.
☐ You'll get over it.
☐ You can do this.
☐ It wasn't that obvious.
☐ This too shall pass.
☐ You're too good for him.
☐ You're too good for her.
☐ I'll never tell.
☐ Don't blame yourself.
☐ There are other fish in the sea.
☐ Tattoo removal is easier now.
☐ You are not your job.
☐ Your mother will never know.
☐ Nothing therapy won't cure.
☐ Just take a mulligan.
☐ Moving home is no big deal.
☐ Don't "should" all over yourself.
☐ At least you know you're right.
☐ You did your best.
☐ Can't win 'em all.
☐ You couldn't have known.
☐ My cousin had that and was fine.
☐ Laughter is the best medicine.
☐ Have faith.
☐ Penicillin clears that up fast.
☐ He wasn't thinking.
☐ She wasn't thinking.
☐ If at first you don't succeed . . .
☐ It's about quality, not quantity.
☐ That's not old, it's vintage.
☐ You're not old, you're vintage.
☐ Things happen for a reason.
☐ It'll look better in the morning.
☐ You can blog about it.
☐ We'll look back later and laugh.
☐ No one will ever know.
☐ Here's a hug.
☐ They don't deserve you.
☐ Every cloud has a silver lining.
☐ It was totally his fault.
☐ It was totally her fault.
☐ A rising tide lifts all boats.
☐ There are specialists for that.
☐ Think of the big picture.
☐ Don't let it bother you so much.
☐ No one saw you trip.
☐ You'll get that promotion soon.
☐ It could've been much worse.
☐ Aim for the stars.
☐ You'll forget about it, I promise.

☐ All publicity is good publicity.
☐ You can always return it.
☐ That was so understandable.
☐ You look great.
☐ You look great for your age.
☐ That happens to everyone.
☐ You made your point.
☐ Who wants that responsibility?
☐ It's not more than you can handle.
☐ Time heals all wounds.
☐ Time wounds all heels.
☐ I'm sure you don't normally do that.
☐ Success or not, you are loved.
☐ It's a journey, not a destination.
☐ It was a long shot anyway.
☐ Lesson learned.
☐ It's not you, it's the economy.
☐ You can always sue.
☐ You're the bigger person.
☐ You still have your honor.
☐ You still have your hair.
☐ Heartbreak makes you wiser.
☐ People will see through that.
☐ You'll be the last one standing.
☐ Don't let it get you down.
☐ It's not forever.
☐ There are always people like that.
☐ Never fear, karma's a bitch.
☐ I think it looks cute.
☐ One door closes, another opens.
☐ It's all part of the plan.
☐ Go ahead, cry it out.
☐ They spelled your name right.
☐ Jobs come, jobs go.
☐ People come, people go.
☐ This must be hard for you.
☐ Time to get on with your life.
☐ Everyone's a critic.
☐ It's for the best.
☐ Don't go there.
☐ It's their loss.
☐ You can focus on your career.
☐ You can focus on your kids.
☐ Didn't kill ya; made ya stronger.
☐ Ours is not to reason why.
☐ Don't take it home with you.
☐ Timing is everything.
☐ You'll eventually love it.
☐ Think positive.
☐ Think denial.

☐ Someday you'll understand.
☐ Single life is actually better.
☐ Always darkest before the dawn.
☐ Just clear the browser history.
☐ You're still young.
☐ He isn't worth it.
☐ She isn't worth it.
☐ Where there's a will . . .
☐ Chalk it up to experience.
☐ Cross that bridge later.
☐ One day at a time.
☐ You can always get it fixed.
☐ Don't sweat the small stuff.
☐ Not over 'til the fat lady sings.
☐ It's all nonsense anyway.
☐ You gotta believe in you.
☐ I believe in you.
☐ Anything is possible.
☐ You reacted with integrity.
☐ You can sell it online.
☐ Don't get mad, get even.
☐ No one can tell it's a knockoff.
☐ Just say no.
☐ Hang in there, baby.
☐ If it's not one thing, it's another.
☐ It'll build character.
☐ It was meant to be.
☐ It wasn't meant to be.
☐ If it's meant to be, it'll happen.
☐ Keep your chin up.
☐ You don't need their approval.
☐ For every hill there's a valley.
☐ I would've done the same.
☐ Life goes on.
☐ Absence makes love stronger.
☐ Can't beat 'em? Join 'em.
☐ Shake it off.
☐ No one heard it.
☐ Better late than never.
☐ Better safe than sorry.
☐ And so it goes.
☐ The first cut is the deepest.
☐ Love hurts.
☐ Love stinks.
☐ Love is overrated.
☐ Soon this'll be a distant memory.
☐ Keep on truckin'.
☐ Quit worrying.
☐ It's water under the bridge.
☐ Don't dwell on it.

☐ Ya gotta do what ya gotta do.
☐ When it rains, it pours.
☐ Every rose has a thorn.
☐ You gave it your best shot.
☐ There, there.
☐ It takes all kinds.
☐ They're just jealous.
☐ It'll come when you're ready.
☐ Nobody mentioned it.
☐ Try to keep it in perspective.
☐ Put on your big girl panties.
☐ Put on your big boy briefs.
☐ There's a lid for every pot.
☐ He's probably out of town.
☐ Her phone is probably dead.
☐ You're better off.
☐ It happens sometimes.
☐ They don't understand you.
☐ It was an honest mistake.
☐ Money can't buy love.
☐ Adversity forges character.
☐ You'll feel better after a bath.
☐ You'll feel better after a drink.
☐ It'll make great memoir material.
☐ Quit blaming yourself.
☐ There's no such thing as normal.
☐ You'll show them.
☐ This will forge your character.
☐ You're a superstar.
☐ Just explain what happened.
☐ Don't compare.
☐ All parents screw up.
☐ All kids screw up.
☐ At least you have your health.
☐ He'll grow out of it.
☐ She'll grow out of it.
☐ Shhh. Shhh. It's okay now.
☐ Pain is temporary.
☐ I agree with you.
☐ One day you'll know why.
☐ You march to your own beat.
☐ Ignore what others think.
☐ Buck up, buckwheat.
☐ Everyone sympathizes.
☐ You're overthinking this.
☐ Get back up on the horse.
☐ Just give it some time.
☐ It's not the end of the world.
☐ It gets better.
☐ Really, it is.

☐ TOTALLY OKAY ☐ PRETTY OKAY ☐ OKAY-ISH

SIGNATURE | MONTH | DAY | YEAR

"OKAY? OKAY. OKAY!"

IT'S GONNA BE OKAY

☐ **RIGHT NOW** ☐ **FAIRLY SOON** ☐ **EVENTUALLY**

☐ It'll grow back.
☐ You'll get over it.
☐ You can do this.
☐ It wasn't that obvious.
☐ This too shall pass.
☐ You're too good for him.
☐ You're too good for her.
☐ I'll never tell.
☐ Don't blame yourself.
☐ There are other fish in the sea.
☐ Tattoo removal is easier now.
☐ You are not your job.
☐ Your mother will never know.
☐ Nothing therapy won't cure.
☐ Just take a mulligan.
☐ Moving home is no big deal.
☐ Don't "should" all over yourself.
☐ At least you know you're right.
☐ You did your best.
☐ Can't win 'em all.
☐ You couldn't have known.
☐ My cousin had that and was fine.
☐ Laughter is the best medicine.
☐ Have faith.
☐ Penicillin clears that up fast.
☐ He wasn't thinking.
☐ She wasn't thinking.
☐ If at first you don't succeed . . .
☐ It's about quality, not quantity.
☐ That's not old, it's vintage.
☐ You're not old, you're vintage.
☐ Things happen for a reason.
☐ It'll look better in the morning.
☐ You can blog about it.
☐ We'll look back later and laugh.
☐ No one will ever know.
☐ Here's a hug.
☐ They don't deserve you.
☐ Every cloud has a silver lining.
☐ It was totally his fault.
☐ It was totally her fault.
☐ A rising tide lifts all boats.
☐ There are specialists for that.
☐ Think of the big picture.
☐ Don't let it bother you so much.
☐ No one saw you trip.
☐ You'll get that promotion soon.
☐ It could've been much worse.
☐ Aim for the stars.
☐ You'll forget about it, I promise.

☐ All publicity is good publicity.
☐ You can always return it.
☐ That was so understandable.
☐ You look great.
☐ You look great for your age.
☐ That happens to everyone.
☐ You made your point.
☐ Who wants that responsibility?
☐ It's not more than you can handle.
☐ Time heals all wounds.
☐ Time wounds all heels.
☐ I'm sure you don't normally do that.
☐ Success or not, you are loved.
☐ It's a journey, not a destination.
☐ It was a long shot anyway.
☐ Lesson learned.
☐ It's not you, it's the economy.
☐ You can always sue.
☐ You're the bigger person.
☐ You still have your honor.
☐ You still have your hair.
☐ Heartbreak makes you wiser.
☐ People will see through that.
☐ You'll be the last one standing.
☐ Don't let it get you down.
☐ It's not forever.
☐ There are always people like that.
☐ Never fear, karma's a bitch.
☐ I think it looks cute.
☐ One door closes, another opens.
☐ It's all part of the plan.
☐ Go ahead, cry it out.
☐ They spelled your name right.
☐ Jobs come, jobs go.
☐ People come, people go.
☐ This must be hard for you.
☐ Time to get on with your life.
☐ Everyone's a critic.
☐ It's for the best.
☐ Don't go there.
☐ It's their loss.
☐ You can focus on your career.
☐ You can focus on your kids.
☐ Didn't kill ya; made ya stronger.
☐ Ours is not to reason why.
☐ Don't take it home with you.
☐ Timing is everything.
☐ You'll eventually love it.
☐ Think positive.
☐ Think denial.

☐ Someday you'll understand.
☐ Single life is actually better.
☐ Always darkest before the dawn.
☐ Just clear the browser history.
☐ You're still young.
☐ He isn't worth it.
☐ She isn't worth it.
☐ Where there's a will . . .
☐ Chalk it up to experience.
☐ Cross that bridge later.
☐ One day at a time.
☐ You can always get it fixed.
☐ Don't sweat the small stuff.
☐ Not over 'til the fat lady sings.
☐ It's all nonsense anyway.
☐ You gotta believe in you.
☐ I believe in you.
☐ Anything is possible.
☐ You reacted with integrity.
☐ You can sell it online.
☐ Don't get mad, get even.
☐ No one can tell it's a knockoff.
☐ Just say no.
☐ Hang in there, baby.
☐ If it's not one thing, it's another.
☐ It'll build character.
☐ It was meant to be.
☐ It wasn't meant to be.
☐ If it's meant to be, it'll happen.
☐ Keep your chin up.
☐ You don't need their approval.
☐ For every hill there's a valley.
☐ I would've done the same.
☐ Life goes on.
☐ Absence makes love stronger.
☐ Can't beat 'em? Join 'em.
☐ Shake it off.
☐ No one heard it.
☐ Better late than never.
☐ Better safe than sorry.
☐ And so it goes.
☐ The first cut is the deepest.
☐ Love hurts.
☐ Love stinks.
☐ Love is overrated.
☐ Soon this'll be a distant memory.
☐ Keep on truckin'.
☐ Quit worrying.
☐ It's water under the bridge.
☐ Don't dwell on it.

☐ Ya gotta do what ya gotta do.
☐ When it rains, it pours.
☐ Every rose has a thorn.
☐ You gave it your best shot.
☐ There, there.
☐ It takes all kinds.
☐ They're just jealous.
☐ It'll come when you're ready.
☐ Nobody mentioned it.
☐ Try to keep it in perspective.
☐ Put on your big girl panties.
☐ Put on your big boy briefs.
☐ There's a lid for every pot.
☐ He's probably out of town.
☐ Her phone is probably dead.
☐ You're better off.
☐ It happens sometimes.
☐ They don't understand you.
☐ It was an honest mistake.
☐ Money can't buy love.
☐ Adversity forges character.
☐ You'll feel better after a bath.
☐ You'll feel better after a drink.
☐ It'll make great memoir material.
☐ Quit blaming yourself.
☐ There's no such thing as normal.
☐ You'll show them.
☐ This will forge your character.
☐ You're a superstar.
☐ Just explain what happened.
☐ Don't compare.
☐ All parents screw up.
☐ All kids screw up.
☐ At least you have your health.
☐ He'll grow out of it.
☐ She'll grow out of it.
☐ Shhh. Shhh. It's okay now.
☐ Pain is temporary.
☐ I agree with you.
☐ One day you'll know why.
☐ You march to your own beat.
☐ Ignore what others think.
☐ Buck up, buckwheat.
☐ Everyone sympathizes.
☐ You're overthinking this.
☐ Get back up on the horse.
☐ Just give it some time.
☐ It's not the end of the world.
☐ It gets better.
☐ Really, it is.

☐ **TOTALLY OKAY** ☐ **PRETTY OKAY** ☐ **OKAY-ISH**

SIGNATURE | MONTH | DAY | YEAR

"OKAY? OKAY. OKAY!"

IT'S GONNA BE OKAY

☐ **RIGHT NOW** ☐ **FAIRLY SOON** ☐ **EVENTUALLY**

☐ It'll grow back.
☐ You'll get over it.
☐ You can do this.
☐ It wasn't that obvious.
☐ This too shall pass.
☐ You're too good for him.
☐ You're too good for her.
☐ I'll never tell.
☐ Don't blame yourself.
☐ There are other fish in the sea.
☐ Tattoo removal is easier now.
☐ You are not your job.
☐ Your mother will never know.
☐ Nothing therapy won't cure.
☐ Just take a mulligan.
☐ Moving home is no big deal.
☐ Don't "should" all over yourself.
☐ At least you know you're right.
☐ You did your best.
☐ Can't win 'em all.
☐ You couldn't have known.
☐ My cousin had that and was fine.
☐ Laughter is the best medicine.
☐ Have faith.
☐ Penicillin clears that up fast.
☐ He wasn't thinking.
☐ She wasn't thinking.
☐ If at first you don't succeed . . .
☐ It's about quality, not quantity.
☐ That's not old, it's vintage.
☐ You're not old, you're vintage.
☐ Things happen for a reason.
☐ It'll look better in the morning.
☐ You can blog about it.
☐ We'll look back later and laugh.
☐ No one will ever know.
☐ Here's a hug.
☐ They don't deserve you.
☐ Every cloud has a silver lining.
☐ It was totally his fault.
☐ It was totally her fault.
☐ A rising tide lifts all boats.
☐ There are specialists for that.
☐ Think of the big picture.
☐ Don't let it bother you so much.
☐ No one saw you trip.
☐ You'll get that promotion soon.
☐ It could've been much worse.
☐ Aim for the stars.
☐ You'll forget about it, I promise.

☐ All publicity is good publicity.
☐ You can always return it.
☐ That was so understandable.
☐ You look great.
☐ You look great for your age.
☐ That happens to everyone.
☐ You made your point.
☐ Who wants that responsibility?
☐ It's not more than you can handle.
☐ Time heals all wounds.
☐ Time wounds all heels.
☐ I'm sure you don't normally do that.
☐ Success or not, you are loved.
☐ It's a journey, not a destination.
☐ It was a long shot anyway.
☐ Lesson learned.
☐ It's not you, it's the economy.
☐ You can always sue.
☐ You're the bigger person.
☐ You still have your honor.
☐ You still have your hair.
☐ Heartbreak makes you wiser.
☐ People will see through that.
☐ You'll be the last one standing.
☐ Don't let it get you down.
☐ It's not forever.
☐ There are always people like that.
☐ Never fear, karma's a bitch.
☐ I think it looks cute.
☐ One door closes, another opens.
☐ It's all part of the plan.
☐ Go ahead, cry it out.
☐ They spelled your name right.
☐ Jobs come, jobs go.
☐ People come, people go.
☐ This must be hard for you.
☐ Time to get on with your life.
☐ Everyone's a critic.
☐ It's for the best.
☐ Don't go there.
☐ It's their loss.
☐ You can focus on your career.
☐ You can focus on your kids.
☐ Didn't kill ya; made ya stronger.
☐ Ours is not to reason why.
☐ Don't take it home with you.
☐ Timing is everything.
☐ You'll eventually love it.
☐ Think positive.
☐ Think denial.

☐ Someday you'll understand.
☐ Single life is actually better.
☐ Always darkest before the dawn.
☐ Just clear the browser history.
☐ You're still young.
☐ He isn't worth it.
☐ She isn't worth it.
☐ Where there's a will . . .
☐ Chalk it up to experience.
☐ Cross that bridge later.
☐ One day at a time.
☐ You can always get it fixed.
☐ Don't sweat the small stuff.
☐ Not over 'til the fat lady sings.
☐ It's all nonsense anyway.
☐ You gotta believe in you.
☐ I believe in you.
☐ Anything is possible.
☐ You reacted with integrity.
☐ You can sell it online.
☐ Don't get mad, get even.
☐ No one can tell it's a knockoff.
☐ Just say no.
☐ Hang in there, baby.
☐ If it's not one thing, it's another.
☐ It'll build character.
☐ It was meant to be.
☐ It wasn't meant to be.
☐ If it's meant to be, it'll happen.
☐ Keep your chin up.
☐ You don't need their approval.
☐ For every hill there's a valley.
☐ I would've done the same.
☐ Life goes on.
☐ Absence makes love stronger.
☐ Can't beat 'em? Join 'em.
☐ Shake it off.
☐ No one heard it.
☐ Better late than never.
☐ Better safe than sorry.
☐ And so it goes.
☐ The first cut is the deepest.
☐ Love hurts.
☐ Love stinks.
☐ Love is overrated.
☐ Soon this'll be a distant memory.
☐ Keep on truckin'.
☐ Quit worrying.
☐ It's water under the bridge.
☐ Don't dwell on it.

☐ Ya gotta do what ya gotta do.
☐ When it rains, it pours.
☐ Every rose has a thorn.
☐ You gave it your best shot.
☐ There, there.
☐ It takes all kinds.
☐ They're just jealous.
☐ It'll come when you're ready.
☐ Nobody mentioned it.
☐ Try to keep it in perspective.
☐ Put on your big girl panties.
☐ Put on your big boy briefs.
☐ There's a lid for every pot.
☐ He's probably out of town.
☐ Her phone is probably dead.
☐ You're better off.
☐ It happens sometimes.
☐ They don't understand you.
☐ It was an honest mistake.
☐ Money can't buy love.
☐ Adversity forges character.
☐ You'll feel better after a bath.
☐ You'll feel better after a drink.
☐ It'll make great memoir material.
☐ Quit blaming yourself.
☐ There's no such thing as normal.
☐ You'll show them.
☐ This will forge your character.
☐ You're a superstar.
☐ Just explain what happened.
☐ Don't compare.
☐ All parents screw up.
☐ All kids screw up.
☐ At least you have your health.
☐ He'll grow out of it.
☐ She'll grow out of it.
☐ Shhh. Shhh. It's okay now.
☐ Pain is temporary.
☐ I agree with you.
☐ One day you'll know why.
☐ You march to your own beat.
☐ Ignore what others think.
☐ Buck up, buckwheat.
☐ Everyone sympathizes.
☐ You're overthinking this.
☐ Get back up on the horse.
☐ Just give it some time.
☐ It's not the end of the world.
☐ It gets better.
☐ Really, it is.

☐ **TOTALLY OKAY** ☐ **PRETTY OKAY** ☐ **OKAY-ISH**

SIGNATURE MONTH DAY YEAR

"OKAY? OKAY. OKAY!"

IT'S GONNA BE OKAY

☐ RIGHT NOW ☐ FAIRLY SOON ☐ EVENTUALLY

- ☐ It'll grow back.
- ☐ You'll get over it.
- ☐ You can do this.
- ☐ It wasn't that obvious.
- ☐ This too shall pass.
- ☐ You're too good for him.
- ☐ You're too good for her.
- ☐ I'll never tell.
- ☐ Don't blame yourself.
- ☐ There are other fish in the sea.
- ☐ Tattoo removal is easier now.
- ☐ You are not your job.
- ☐ Your mother will never know.
- ☐ Nothing therapy won't cure.
- ☐ Just take a mulligan.
- ☐ Moving home is no big deal.
- ☐ Don't "should" all over yourself.
- ☐ At least you know you're right.
- ☐ You did your best.
- ☐ Can't win 'em all.
- ☐ You couldn't have known.
- ☐ My cousin had that and was fine.
- ☐ Laughter is the best medicine.
- ☐ Have faith.
- ☐ Penicillin clears that up fast.
- ☐ He wasn't thinking.
- ☐ She wasn't thinking.
- ☐ If at first you don't succeed . . .
- ☐ It's about quality, not quantity.
- ☐ That's not old, it's vintage.
- ☐ You're not old, you're vintage.
- ☐ Things happen for a reason.
- ☐ It'll look better in the morning.
- ☐ You can blog about it.
- ☐ We'll look back later and laugh.
- ☐ No one will ever know.
- ☐ Here's a hug.
- ☐ They don't deserve you.
- ☐ Every cloud has a silver lining.
- ☐ It was totally his fault.
- ☐ It was totally her fault.
- ☐ A rising tide lifts all boats.
- ☐ There are specialists for that.
- ☐ Think of the big picture.
- ☐ Don't let it bother you so much.
- ☐ No one saw you trip.
- ☐ You'll get that promotion soon.
- ☐ It could've been much worse.
- ☐ Aim for the stars.
- ☐ You'll forget about it, I promise.

- ☐ All publicity is good publicity.
- ☐ You can always return it.
- ☐ That was so understandable.
- ☐ You look great.
- ☐ You look great for your age.
- ☐ That happens to everyone.
- ☐ You made your point.
- ☐ Who wants that responsibility?
- ☐ It's not more than you can handle.
- ☐ Time heals all wounds.
- ☐ Time wounds all heels.
- ☐ I'm sure you don't normally do that.
- ☐ Success or not, you are loved.
- ☐ It's a journey, not a destination.
- ☐ It was a long shot anyway.
- ☐ Lesson learned.
- ☐ It's not you, it's the economy.
- ☐ You can always sue.
- ☐ You're the bigger person.
- ☐ You still have your honor.
- ☐ You still have your hair.
- ☐ Heartbreak makes you wiser.
- ☐ People will see through that.
- ☐ You'll be the last one standing.
- ☐ Don't let it get you down.
- ☐ It's not forever.
- ☐ There are always people like that.
- ☐ Never fear, karma's a bitch.
- ☐ I think it looks cute.
- ☐ One door closes, another opens.
- ☐ It's all part of the plan.
- ☐ Go ahead, cry it out.
- ☐ They spelled your name right.
- ☐ Jobs come, jobs go.
- ☐ People come, people go.
- ☐ This must be hard for you.
- ☐ Time to get on with your life.
- ☐ Everyone's a critic.
- ☐ It's for the best.
- ☐ Don't go there.
- ☐ It's their loss.
- ☐ You can focus on your career.
- ☐ You can focus on your kids.
- ☐ Didn't kill ya; made ya stronger.
- ☐ Ours is not to reason why.
- ☐ Don't take it home with you.
- ☐ Timing is everything.
- ☐ You'll eventually love it.
- ☐ Think positive.
- ☐ Think denial.

- ☐ Someday you'll understand.
- ☐ Single life is actually better.
- ☐ Always darkest before the dawn.
- ☐ Just clear the browser history.
- ☐ You're still young.
- ☐ He isn't worth it.
- ☐ She isn't worth it.
- ☐ Where there's a will . . .
- ☐ Chalk it up to experience.
- ☐ Cross that bridge later.
- ☐ One day at a time.
- ☐ You can always get it fixed.
- ☐ Don't sweat the small stuff.
- ☐ Not over 'til the fat lady sings.
- ☐ It's all nonsense anyway.
- ☐ You gotta believe in you.
- ☐ I believe in you.
- ☐ Anything is possible.
- ☐ You reacted with integrity.
- ☐ You can sell it online.
- ☐ Don't get mad, get even.
- ☐ No one can tell it's a knockoff.
- ☐ Just say no.
- ☐ Hang in there, baby.
- ☐ If it's not one thing, it's another.
- ☐ It'll build character.
- ☐ It was meant to be.
- ☐ It wasn't meant to be.
- ☐ If it's meant to be, it'll happen.
- ☐ Keep your chin up.
- ☐ You don't need their approval.
- ☐ For every hill there's a valley.
- ☐ I would've done the same.
- ☐ Life goes on.
- ☐ Absence makes love stronger.
- ☐ Can't beat 'em? Join 'em.
- ☐ Shake it off.
- ☐ No one heard it.
- ☐ Better late than never.
- ☐ Better safe than sorry.
- ☐ And so it goes.
- ☐ The first cut is the deepest.
- ☐ Love hurts.
- ☐ Love stinks.
- ☐ Love is overrated.
- ☐ Soon this'll be a distant memory.
- ☐ Keep on truckin'.
- ☐ Quit worrying.
- ☐ It's water under the bridge.
- ☐ Don't dwell on it.

- ☐ Ya gotta do what ya gotta do.
- ☐ When it rains, it pours.
- ☐ Every rose has a thorn.
- ☐ You gave it your best shot.
- ☐ There, there.
- ☐ It takes all kinds.
- ☐ They're just jealous.
- ☐ It'll come when you're ready.
- ☐ Nobody mentioned it.
- ☐ Try to keep it in perspective.
- ☐ Put on your big girl panties.
- ☐ Put on your big boy briefs.
- ☐ There's a lid for every pot.
- ☐ He's probably out of town.
- ☐ Her phone is probably dead.
- ☐ You're better off.
- ☐ It happens sometimes.
- ☐ They don't understand you.
- ☐ It was an honest mistake.
- ☐ Money can't buy love.
- ☐ Adversity forges character.
- ☐ You'll feel better after a bath.
- ☐ You'll feel better after a drink.
- ☐ It'll make great memoir material.
- ☐ Quit blaming yourself.
- ☐ There's no such thing as normal.
- ☐ You'll show them.
- ☐ This will forge your character.
- ☐ You're a superstar.
- ☐ Just explain what happened.
- ☐ Don't compare.
- ☐ All parents screw up.
- ☐ All kids screw up.
- ☐ At least you have your health.
- ☐ He'll grow out of it.
- ☐ She'll grow out of it.
- ☐ Shhh. Shhh. It's okay now.
- ☐ Pain is temporary.
- ☐ I agree with you.
- ☐ One day you'll know why.
- ☐ You march to your own beat.
- ☐ Ignore what others think.
- ☐ Buck up, buckwheat.
- ☐ Everyone sympathizes.
- ☐ You're overthinking this.
- ☐ Get back up on the horse.
- ☐ Just give it some time.
- ☐ It's not the end of the world.
- ☐ It gets better.
- ☐ Really, it is.

☐ TOTALLY OKAY ☐ PRETTY OKAY ☐ OKAY-ISH

SIGNATURE	MONTH	DAY	YEAR

"OKAY? OKAY. OKAY!"

IT'S GONNA BE OKAY

☐ **RIGHT NOW** ☐ **FAIRLY SOON** ☐ **EVENTUALLY**

☐ It'll grow back.
☐ You'll get over it.
☐ You can do this.
☐ It wasn't that obvious.
☐ This too shall pass.
☐ You're too good for him.
☐ You're too good for her.
☐ I'll never tell.
☐ Don't blame yourself.
☐ There are other fish in the sea.
☐ Tattoo removal is easier now.
☐ You are not your job.
☐ Your mother will never know.
☐ Nothing therapy won't cure.
☐ Just take a mulligan.
☐ Moving home is no big deal.
☐ Don't "should" all over yourself.
☐ At least you know you're right.
☐ You did your best.
☐ Can't win 'em all.
☐ You couldn't have known.
☐ My cousin had that and was fine.
☐ Laughter is the best medicine.
☐ Have faith.
☐ Penicillin clears that up fast.
☐ He wasn't thinking.
☐ She wasn't thinking.
☐ If at first you don't succeed . . .
☐ It's about quality, not quantity.
☐ That's not old, it's vintage.
☐ You're not old, you're vintage.
☐ Things happen for a reason.
☐ It'll look better in the morning.
☐ You can blog about it.
☐ We'll look back later and laugh.
☐ No one will ever know.
☐ Here's a hug.
☐ They don't deserve you.
☐ Every cloud has a silver lining.
☐ It was totally his fault.
☐ It was totally her fault.
☐ A rising tide lifts all boats.
☐ There are specialists for that.
☐ Think of the big picture.
☐ Don't let it bother you so much.
☐ No one saw you trip.
☐ You'll get that promotion soon.
☐ It could've been much worse.
☐ Aim for the stars.
☐ You'll forget about it, I promise.

☐ All publicity is good publicity.
☐ You can always return it.
☐ That was so understandable.
☐ You look great.
☐ You look great for your age.
☐ That happens to everyone.
☐ You made your point.
☐ Who wants that responsibility?
☐ It's not more than you can handle.
☐ Time heals all wounds.
☐ Time wounds all heels.
☐ I'm sure you don't normally do that.
☐ Success or not, you are loved.
☐ It's a journey, not a destination.
☐ It was a long shot anyway.
☐ Lesson learned.
☐ It's not you, it's the economy.
☐ You can always sue.
☐ You're the bigger person.
☐ You still have your honor.
☐ You still have your hair.
☐ Heartbreak makes you wiser.
☐ People will see through that.
☐ You'll be the last one standing.
☐ Don't let it get you down.
☐ It's not forever.
☐ There are always people like that.
☐ Never fear, karma's a bitch.
☐ I think it looks cute.
☐ One door closes, another opens.
☐ It's all part of the plan.
☐ Go ahead, cry it out.
☐ They spelled your name right.
☐ Jobs come, jobs go.
☐ People come, people go.
☐ This must be hard for you.
☐ Time to get on with your life.
☐ Everyone's a critic.
☐ It's for the best.
☐ Don't go there.
☐ It's their loss.
☐ You can focus on your career.
☐ You can focus on your kids.
☐ Didn't kill ya; made ya stronger.
☐ Ours is not to reason why.
☐ Don't take it home with you.
☐ Timing is everything.
☐ You'll eventually love it.
☐ Think positive.
☐ Think denial.

☐ Someday you'll understand.
☐ Single life is actually better.
☐ Always darkest before the dawn.
☐ Just clear the browser history.
☐ You're still young.
☐ He isn't worth it.
☐ She isn't worth it.
☐ Where there's a will . . .
☐ Chalk it up to experience.
☐ Cross that bridge later.
☐ One day at a time.
☐ You can always get it fixed.
☐ Don't sweat the small stuff.
☐ Not over 'til the fat lady sings.
☐ It's all nonsense anyway.
☐ You gotta believe in you.
☐ I believe in you.
☐ Anything is possible.
☐ You reacted with integrity.
☐ You can sell it online.
☐ Don't get mad, get even.
☐ No one can tell it's a knockoff.
☐ Just say no.
☐ Hang in there, baby.
☐ If it's not one thing, it's another.
☐ It'll build character.
☐ It was meant to be.
☐ It wasn't meant to be.
☐ If it's meant to be, it'll happen.
☐ Keep your chin up.
☐ You don't need their approval.
☐ For every hill there's a valley.
☐ I would've done the same.
☐ Life goes on.
☐ Absence makes love stronger.
☐ Can't beat 'em? Join 'em.
☐ Shake it off.
☐ No one heard it.
☐ Better late than never.
☐ Better safe than sorry.
☐ And so it goes.
☐ The first cut is the deepest.
☐ Love hurts.
☐ Love stinks.
☐ Love is overrated.
☐ Soon this'll be a distant memory.
☐ Keep on truckin'.
☐ Quit worrying.
☐ It's water under the bridge.
☐ Don't dwell on it.

☐ Ya gotta do what ya gotta do.
☐ When it rains, it pours.
☐ Every rose has a thorn.
☐ You gave it your best shot.
☐ There, there.
☐ It takes all kinds.
☐ They're just jealous.
☐ It'll come when you're ready.
☐ Nobody mentioned it.
☐ Try to keep it in perspective.
☐ Put on your big girl panties.
☐ Put on your big boy briefs.
☐ There's a lid for every pot.
☐ He's probably out of town.
☐ Her phone is probably dead.
☐ You're better off.
☐ It happens sometimes.
☐ They don't understand you.
☐ It was an honest mistake.
☐ Money can't buy love.
☐ Adversity forges character.
☐ You'll feel better after a bath.
☐ You'll feel better after a drink.
☐ It'll make great memoir material.
☐ Quit blaming yourself.
☐ There's no such thing as normal.
☐ You'll show them.
☐ This will forge your character.
☐ You're a superstar.
☐ Just explain what happened.
☐ Don't compare.
☐ All parents screw up.
☐ All kids screw up.
☐ At least you have your health.
☐ He'll grow out of it.
☐ She'll grow out of it.
☐ Shhh. Shhh. It's okay now.
☐ Pain is temporary.
☐ I agree with you.
☐ One day you'll know why.
☐ You march to your own beat.
☐ Ignore what others think.
☐ Buck up, buckwheat.
☐ Everyone sympathizes.
☐ You're overthinking this.
☐ Get back up on the horse.
☐ Just give it some time.
☐ It's not the end of the world.
☐ It gets better.
☐ Really, it is.

☐ **TOTALLY OKAY** ☐ **PRETTY OKAY** ☐ **OKAY-ISH**

SIGNATURE MONTH DAY YEAR

"OKAY? OKAY. OKAY!"

IT'S GONNA BE OKAY

☐ **RIGHT NOW** ☐ **FAIRLY SOON** ☐ **EVENTUALLY**

☐ It'll grow back.
☐ You'll get over it.
☐ You can do this.
☐ It wasn't that obvious.
☐ This too shall pass.
☐ You're too good for him.
☐ You're too good for her.
☐ I'll never tell.
☐ Don't blame yourself.
☐ There are other fish in the sea.
☐ Tattoo removal is easier now.
☐ You are not your job.
☐ Your mother will never know.
☐ Nothing therapy won't cure.
☐ Just take a mulligan.
☐ Moving home is no big deal.
☐ Don't "should" all over yourself.
☐ At least you know you're right.
☐ You did your best.
☐ Can't win 'em all.
☐ You couldn't have known.
☐ My cousin had that and was fine.
☐ Laughter is the best medicine.
☐ Have faith.
☐ Penicillin clears that up fast.
☐ He wasn't thinking.
☐ She wasn't thinking.
☐ If at first you don't succeed . . .
☐ It's about quality, not quantity.
☐ That's not old, it's vintage.
☐ You're not old, you're vintage.
☐ Things happen for a reason.
☐ It'll look better in the morning.
☐ You can blog about it.
☐ We'll look back later and laugh.
☐ No one will ever know.
☐ Here's a hug.
☐ They don't deserve you.
☐ Every cloud has a silver lining.
☐ It was totally his fault.
☐ It was totally her fault.
☐ A rising tide lifts all boats.
☐ There are specialists for that.
☐ Think of the big picture.
☐ Don't let it bother you so much.
☐ No one saw you trip.
☐ You'll get that promotion soon.
☐ It could've been much worse.
☐ Aim for the stars.
☐ You'll forget about it, I promise.

☐ All publicity is good publicity.
☐ You can always return it.
☐ That was so understandable.
☐ You look great.
☐ You look great for your age.
☐ That happens to everyone.
☐ You made your point.
☐ Who wants that responsibility?
☐ It's not more than you can handle.
☐ Time heals all wounds.
☐ Time wounds all heels.
☐ I'm sure you don't normally do that.
☐ Success or not, you are loved.
☐ It's a journey, not a destination.
☐ It was a long shot anyway.
☐ Lesson learned.
☐ It's not you, it's the economy.
☐ You can always sue.
☐ You're the bigger person.
☐ You still have your honor.
☐ You still have your hair.
☐ Heartbreak makes you wiser.
☐ People will see through that.
☐ You'll be the last one standing.
☐ Don't let it get you down.
☐ It's not forever.
☐ There are always people like that.
☐ Never fear, karma's a bitch.
☐ I think it looks cute.
☐ One door closes, another opens.
☐ It's all part of the plan.
☐ Go ahead, cry it out.
☐ They spelled your name right.
☐ Jobs come, jobs go.
☐ People come, people go.
☐ This must be hard for you.
☐ Time to get on with your life.
☐ Everyone's a critic.
☐ It's for the best.
☐ Don't go there.
☐ It's their loss.
☐ You can focus on your career.
☐ You can focus on your kids.
☐ Didn't kill ya; made ya stronger.
☐ Ours is not to reason why.
☐ Don't take it home with you.
☐ Timing is everything.
☐ You'll eventually love it.
☐ Think positive.
☐ Think denial.

☐ Someday you'll understand.
☐ Single life is actually better.
☐ Always darkest before the dawn.
☐ Just clear the browser history.
☐ You're still young.
☐ He isn't worth it.
☐ She isn't worth it.
☐ Where there's a will . . .
☐ Chalk it up to experience.
☐ Cross that bridge later.
☐ One day at a time.
☐ You can always get it fixed.
☐ Don't sweat the small stuff.
☐ Not over 'til the fat lady sings.
☐ It's all nonsense anyway.
☐ You gotta believe in you.
☐ I believe in you.
☐ Anything is possible.
☐ You reacted with integrity.
☐ You can sell it online.
☐ Don't get mad, get even.
☐ No one can tell it's a knockoff.
☐ Just say no.
☐ Hang in there, baby.
☐ If it's not one thing, it's another.
☐ It'll build character.
☐ It was meant to be.
☐ It wasn't meant to be.
☐ If it's meant to be, it'll happen.
☐ Keep your chin up.
☐ You don't need their approval.
☐ For every hill there's a valley.
☐ I would've done the same.
☐ Life goes on.
☐ Absence makes love stronger.
☐ Can't beat 'em? Join 'em.
☐ Shake it off.
☐ No one heard it.
☐ Better late than never.
☐ Better safe than sorry.
☐ And so it goes.
☐ The first cut is the deepest.
☐ Love hurts.
☐ Love stinks.
☐ Love is overrated.
☐ Soon this'll be a distant memory.
☐ Keep on truckin'.
☐ Quit worrying.
☐ It's water under the bridge.
☐ Don't dwell on it.

☐ Ya gotta do what ya gotta do.
☐ When it rains, it pours.
☐ Every rose has a thorn.
☐ You gave it your best shot.
☐ There, there.
☐ It takes all kinds.
☐ They're just jealous.
☐ It'll come when you're ready.
☐ Nobody mentioned it.
☐ Try to keep it in perspective.
☐ Put on your big girl panties.
☐ Put on your big boy briefs.
☐ There's a lid for every pot.
☐ He's probably out of town.
☐ Her phone is probably dead.
☐ You're better off.
☐ It happens sometimes.
☐ They don't understand you.
☐ It was an honest mistake.
☐ Money can't buy love.
☐ Adversity forges character.
☐ You'll feel better after a bath.
☐ You'll feel better after a drink.
☐ It'll make great memoir material.
☐ Quit blaming yourself.
☐ There's no such thing as normal.
☐ You'll show them.
☐ This will forge your character.
☐ You're a superstar.
☐ Just explain what happened.
☐ Don't compare.
☐ All parents screw up.
☐ All kids screw up.
☐ At least you have your health.
☐ He'll grow out of it.
☐ She'll grow out of it.
☐ Shhh. Shhh. It's okay now.
☐ Pain is temporary.
☐ I agree with you.
☐ One day you'll know why.
☐ You march to your own beat.
☐ Ignore what others think.
☐ Buck up, buckwheat.
☐ Everyone sympathizes.
☐ You're overthinking this.
☐ Get back up on the horse.
☐ Just give it some time.
☐ It's not the end of the world.
☐ It gets better.
☐ Really, it is.

☐ **TOTALLY OKAY** ☐ **PRETTY OKAY** ☐ **OKAY-ISH**

SIGNATURE

MONTH : DAY : YEAR

"OKAY? OKAY. OKAY!"

IT'S GONNA BE OKAY

☐ **RIGHT NOW** ☐ **FAIRLY SOON** ☐ **EVENTUALLY**

☐ It'll grow back.
☐ You'll get over it.
☐ You can do this.
☐ It wasn't that obvious.
☐ This too shall pass.
☐ You're too good for him.
☐ You're too good for her.
☐ I'll never tell.
☐ Don't blame yourself.
☐ There are other fish in the sea.
☐ Tattoo removal is easier now.
☐ You are not your job.
☐ Your mother will never know.
☐ Nothing therapy won't cure.
☐ Just take a mulligan.
☐ Moving home is no big deal.
☐ Don't "should" all over yourself.
☐ At least you know you're right.
☐ You did your best.
☐ Can't win 'em all.
☐ You couldn't have known.
☐ My cousin had that and was fine.
☐ Laughter is the best medicine.
☐ Have faith.
☐ Penicillin clears that up fast.
☐ He wasn't thinking.
☐ She wasn't thinking.
☐ If at first you don't succeed . . .
☐ It's about quality, not quantity.
☐ That's not old, it's vintage.
☐ You're not old, you're vintage.
☐ Things happen for a reason.
☐ It'll look better in the morning.
☐ You can blog about it.
☐ We'll look back later and laugh.
☐ No one will ever know.
☐ Here's a hug.
☐ They don't deserve you.
☐ Every cloud has a silver lining.
☐ It was totally his fault.
☐ It was totally her fault.
☐ A rising tide lifts all boats.
☐ There are specialists for that.
☐ Think of the big picture.
☐ Don't let it bother you so much.
☐ No one saw you trip.
☐ You'll get that promotion soon.
☐ It could've been much worse.
☐ Aim for the stars.
☐ You'll forget about it, I promise.

☐ All publicity is good publicity.
☐ You can always return it.
☐ That was so understandable.
☐ You look great.
☐ You look great for your age.
☐ That happens to everyone.
☐ You made your point.
☐ Who wants that responsibility?
☐ It's not more than you can handle.
☐ Time heals all wounds.
☐ Time wounds all heels.
☐ I'm sure you don't normally do that.
☐ Success or not, you are loved.
☐ It's a journey, not a destination.
☐ It was a long shot anyway.
☐ Lesson learned.
☐ It's not you, it's the economy.
☐ You can always sue.
☐ You're the bigger person.
☐ You still have your honor.
☐ You still have your hair.
☐ Heartbreak makes you wiser.
☐ People will see through that.
☐ You'll be the last one standing.
☐ Don't let it get you down.
☐ It's not forever.
☐ There are always people like that.
☐ Never fear, karma's a bitch.
☐ I think it looks cute.
☐ One door closes, another opens.
☐ It's all part of the plan.
☐ Go ahead, cry it out.
☐ They spelled your name right.
☐ Jobs come, jobs go.
☐ People come, people go.
☐ This must be hard for you.
☐ Time to get on with your life.
☐ Everyone's a critic.
☐ It's for the best.
☐ Don't go there.
☐ It's their loss.
☐ You can focus on your career.
☐ You can focus on your kids.
☐ Didn't kill ya; made ya stronger.
☐ Ours is not to reason why.
☐ Don't take it home with you.
☐ Timing is everything.
☐ You'll eventually love it.
☐ Think positive.
☐ Think denial.

☐ Someday you'll understand.
☐ Single life is actually better.
☐ Always darkest before the dawn.
☐ Just clear the browser history.
☐ You're still young.
☐ He isn't worth it.
☐ She isn't worth it.
☐ Where there's a will . . .
☐ Chalk it up to experience.
☐ Cross that bridge later.
☐ One day at a time.
☐ You can always get it fixed.
☐ Don't sweat the small stuff.
☐ Not over 'til the fat lady sings.
☐ It's all nonsense anyway.
☐ You gotta believe in you.
☐ I believe in you.
☐ Anything is possible.
☐ You reacted with integrity.
☐ You can sell it online.
☐ Don't get mad, get even.
☐ No one can tell it's a knockoff.
☐ Just say no.
☐ Hang in there, baby.
☐ If it's not one thing, it's another.
☐ It'll build character.
☐ It was meant to be.
☐ It wasn't meant to be.
☐ If it's meant to be, it'll happen.
☐ Keep your chin up.
☐ You don't need their approval.
☐ For every hill there's a valley.
☐ I would've done the same.
☐ Life goes on.
☐ Absence makes love stronger.
☐ Can't beat 'em? Join 'em.
☐ Shake it off.
☐ No one heard it.
☐ Better late than never.
☐ Better safe than sorry.
☐ And so it goes.
☐ The first cut is the deepest.
☐ Love hurts.
☐ Love stinks.
☐ Love is overrated.
☐ Soon this'll be a distant memory.
☐ Keep on truckin'.
☐ Quit worrying.
☐ It's water under the bridge.
☐ Don't dwell on it.

☐ Ya gotta do what ya gotta do.
☐ When it rains, it pours.
☐ Every rose has a thorn.
☐ You gave it your best shot.
☐ There, there.
☐ It takes all kinds.
☐ They're just jealous.
☐ It'll come when you're ready.
☐ Nobody mentioned it.
☐ Try to keep it in perspective.
☐ Put on your big girl panties.
☐ Put on your big boy briefs.
☐ There's a lid for every pot.
☐ He's probably out of town.
☐ Her phone is probably dead.
☐ You're better off.
☐ It happens sometimes.
☐ They don't understand you.
☐ It was an honest mistake.
☐ Money can't buy love.
☐ Adversity forges character.
☐ You'll feel better after a bath.
☐ You'll feel better after a drink.
☐ It'll make great memoir material.
☐ Quit blaming yourself.
☐ There's no such thing as normal.
☐ You'll show them.
☐ This will forge your character.
☐ You're a superstar.
☐ Just explain what happened.
☐ Don't compare.
☐ All parents screw up.
☐ All kids screw up.
☐ At least you have your health.
☐ He'll grow out of it.
☐ She'll grow out of it.
☐ Shhh. Shhh. It's okay now.
☐ Pain is temporary.
☐ I agree with you.
☐ One day you'll know why.
☐ You march to your own beat.
☐ Ignore what others think.
☐ Buck up, buckwheat.
☐ Everyone sympathizes.
☐ You're overthinking this.
☐ Get back up on the horse.
☐ Just give it some time.
☐ It's not the end of the world.
☐ It gets better.
☐ Really, it is.

☐ **TOTALLY OKAY** ☐ **PRETTY OKAY** ☐ **OKAY-ISH**

SIGNATURE | MONTH | DAY | YEAR

"OKAY? OKAY. OKAY!"

IT'S GONNA BE OKAY

☐ **RIGHT NOW** ☐ **FAIRLY SOON** ☐ **EVENTUALLY**

☐ It'll grow back.
☐ You'll get over it.
☐ You can do this.
☐ It wasn't that obvious.
☐ This too shall pass.
☐ You're too good for him.
☐ You're too good for her.
☐ I'll never tell.
☐ Don't blame yourself.
☐ There are other fish in the sea.
☐ Tattoo removal is easier now.
☐ You are not your job.
☐ Your mother will never know.
☐ Nothing therapy won't cure.
☐ Just take a mulligan.
☐ Moving home is no big deal.
☐ Don't "should" all over yourself.
☐ At least you know you're right.
☐ You did your best.
☐ Can't win 'em all.
☐ You couldn't have known.
☐ My cousin had that and was fine.
☐ Laughter is the best medicine.
☐ Have faith.
☐ Penicillin clears that up fast.
☐ He wasn't thinking.
☐ She wasn't thinking.
☐ If at first you don't succeed . . .
☐ It's about quality, not quantity.
☐ That's not old, it's vintage.
☐ You're not old, you're vintage.
☐ Things happen for a reason.
☐ It'll look better in the morning.
☐ You can blog about it.
☐ We'll look back later and laugh.
☐ No one will ever know.
☐ Here's a hug.
☐ They don't deserve you.
☐ Every cloud has a silver lining.
☐ It was totally his fault.
☐ It was totally her fault.
☐ A rising tide lifts all boats.
☐ There are specialists for that.
☐ Think of the big picture.
☐ Don't let it bother you so much.
☐ No one saw you trip.
☐ You'll get that promotion soon.
☐ It could've been much worse.
☐ Aim for the stars.
☐ You'll forget about it, I promise.

☐ All publicity is good publicity.
☐ You can always return it.
☐ That was so understandable.
☐ You look great.
☐ You look great for your age.
☐ That happens to everyone.
☐ You made your point.
☐ Who wants that responsibility?
☐ It's not more than you can handle.
☐ Time heals all wounds.
☐ Time wounds all heels.
☐ I'm sure you don't normally do that.
☐ Success or not, you are loved.
☐ It's a journey, not a destination.
☐ It was a long shot anyway.
☐ Lesson learned.
☐ It's not you, it's the economy.
☐ You can always sue.
☐ You're the bigger person.
☐ You still have your honor.
☐ You still have your hair.
☐ Heartbreak makes you wiser.
☐ People will see through that.
☐ You'll be the last one standing.
☐ Don't let it get you down.
☐ It's not forever.
☐ There are always people like that.
☐ Never fear, karma's a bitch.
☐ I think it looks cute.
☐ One door closes, another opens.
☐ It's all part of the plan.
☐ Go ahead, cry it out.
☐ They spelled your name right.
☐ Jobs come, jobs go.
☐ People come, people go.
☐ This must be hard for you.
☐ Time to get on with your life.
☐ Everyone's a critic.
☐ It's for the best.
☐ Don't go there.
☐ It's their loss.
☐ You can focus on your career.
☐ You can focus on your kids.
☐ Didn't kill ya; made ya stronger.
☐ Ours is not to reason why.
☐ Don't take it home with you.
☐ Timing is everything.
☐ You'll eventually love it.
☐ Think positive.
☐ Think denial.

☐ Someday you'll understand.
☐ Single life is actually better.
☐ Always darkest before the dawn.
☐ Just clear the browser history.
☐ You're still young.
☐ He isn't worth it.
☐ She isn't worth it.
☐ Where there's a will . . .
☐ Chalk it up to experience.
☐ Cross that bridge later.
☐ One day at a time.
☐ You can always get it fixed.
☐ Don't sweat the small stuff.
☐ Not over 'til the fat lady sings.
☐ It's all nonsense anyway.
☐ You gotta believe in you.
☐ I believe in you.
☐ Anything is possible.
☐ You reacted with integrity.
☐ You can sell it online.
☐ Don't get mad, get even.
☐ No one can tell it's a knockoff.
☐ Just say no.
☐ Hang in there, baby.
☐ If it's not one thing, it's another.
☐ It'll build character.
☐ It was meant to be.
☐ It wasn't meant to be.
☐ If it's meant to be, it'll happen.
☐ Keep your chin up.
☐ You don't need their approval.
☐ For every hill there's a valley.
☐ I would've done the same.
☐ Life goes on.
☐ Absence makes love stronger.
☐ Can't beat 'em? Join 'em.
☐ Shake it off.
☐ No one heard it.
☐ Better late than never.
☐ Better safe than sorry.
☐ And so it goes.
☐ The first cut is the deepest.
☐ Love hurts.
☐ Love stinks.
☐ Love is overrated.
☐ Soon this'll be a distant memory.
☐ Keep on truckin'.
☐ Quit worrying.
☐ It's water under the bridge.
☐ Don't dwell on it.

☐ Ya gotta do what ya gotta do.
☐ When it rains, it pours.
☐ Every rose has a thorn.
☐ You gave it your best shot.
☐ There, there.
☐ It takes all kinds.
☐ They're just jealous.
☐ It'll come when you're ready.
☐ Nobody mentioned it.
☐ Try to keep it in perspective.
☐ Put on your big girl panties.
☐ Put on your big boy briefs.
☐ There's a lid for every pot.
☐ He's probably out of town.
☐ Her phone is probably dead.
☐ You're better off.
☐ It happens sometimes.
☐ They don't understand you.
☐ It was an honest mistake.
☐ Money can't buy love.
☐ Adversity forges character.
☐ You'll feel better after a bath.
☐ You'll feel better after a drink.
☐ It'll make great memoir material.
☐ Quit blaming yourself.
☐ There's no such thing as normal.
☐ You'll show them.
☐ This will forge your character.
☐ You're a superstar.
☐ Just explain what happened.
☐ Don't compare.
☐ All parents screw up.
☐ All kids screw up.
☐ At least you have your health.
☐ He'll grow out of it.
☐ She'll grow out of it.
☐ Shhh. Shhh. It's okay now.
☐ Pain is temporary.
☐ I agree with you.
☐ One day you'll know why.
☐ You march to your own beat.
☐ Ignore what others think.
☐ Buck up, buckwheat.
☐ Everyone sympathizes.
☐ You're overthinking this.
☐ Get back up on the horse.
☐ Just give it some time.
☐ It's not the end of the world.
☐ It gets better.
☐ Really, it is.

☐ **TOTALLY OKAY** ☐ **PRETTY OKAY** ☐ **OKAY-ISH**

SIGNATURE

MONTH : DAY : YEAR

"OKAY? OKAY. OKAY!"

IT'S GONNA BE OKAY

☐ **RIGHT NOW** ☐ **FAIRLY SOON** ☐ **EVENTUALLY**

☐ It'll grow back.
☐ You'll get over it.
☐ You can do this.
☐ It wasn't that obvious.
☐ This too shall pass.
☐ You're too good for him.
☐ You're too good for her.
☐ I'll never tell.
☐ Don't blame yourself.
☐ There are other fish in the sea.
☐ Tattoo removal is easier now.
☐ You are not your job.
☐ Your mother will never know.
☐ Nothing therapy won't cure.
☐ Just take a mulligan.
☐ Moving home is no big deal.
☐ Don't "should" all over yourself.
☐ At least you know you're right.
☐ You did your best.
☐ Can't win 'em all.
☐ You couldn't have known.
☐ My cousin had that and was fine.
☐ Laughter is the best medicine.
☐ Have faith.
☐ Penicillin clears that up fast.
☐ He wasn't thinking.
☐ She wasn't thinking.
☐ If at first you don't succeed . . .
☐ It's about quality, not quantity.
☐ That's not old, it's vintage.
☐ You're not old, you're vintage.
☐ Things happen for a reason.
☐ It'll look better in the morning.
☐ You can blog about it.
☐ We'll look back later and laugh.
☐ No one will ever know.
☐ Here's a hug.
☐ They don't deserve you.
☐ Every cloud has a silver lining.
☐ It was totally his fault.
☐ It was totally her fault.
☐ A rising tide lifts all boats.
☐ There are specialists for that.
☐ Think of the big picture.
☐ Don't let it bother you so much.
☐ No one saw you trip.
☐ You'll get that promotion soon.
☐ It could've been much worse.
☐ Aim for the stars.
☐ You'll forget about it, I promise.

☐ All publicity is good publicity.
☐ You can always return it.
☐ That was so understandable.
☐ You look great.
☐ You look great for your age.
☐ That happens to everyone.
☐ You made your point.
☐ Who wants that responsibility?
☐ It's not more than you can handle.
☐ Time heals all wounds.
☐ Time wounds all heels.
☐ I'm sure you don't normally do that.
☐ Success or not, you are loved.
☐ It's a journey, not a destination.
☐ It was a long shot anyway.
☐ Lesson learned.
☐ It's not you, it's the economy.
☐ You can always sue.
☐ You're the bigger person.
☐ You still have your honor.
☐ You still have your hair.
☐ Heartbreak makes you wiser.
☐ People will see through that.
☐ You'll be the last one standing.
☐ Don't let it get you down.
☐ It's not forever.
☐ There are always people like that.
☐ Never fear, karma's a bitch.
☐ I think it looks cute.
☐ One door closes, another opens.
☐ It's all part of the plan.
☐ Go ahead, cry it out.
☐ They spelled your name right.
☐ Jobs come, jobs go.
☐ People come, people go.
☐ This must be hard for you.
☐ Time to get on with your life.
☐ Everyone's a critic.
☐ It's for the best.
☐ Don't go there.
☐ It's their loss.
☐ You can focus on your career.
☐ You can focus on your kids.
☐ Didn't kill ya; made ya stronger.
☐ Ours is not to reason why.
☐ Don't take it home with you.
☐ Timing is everything.
☐ You'll eventually love it.
☐ Think positive.
☐ Think denial.

☐ Someday you'll understand.
☐ Single life is actually better.
☐ Always darkest before the dawn.
☐ Just clear the browser history.
☐ You're still young.
☐ He isn't worth it.
☐ She isn't worth it.
☐ Where there's a will . . .
☐ Chalk it up to experience.
☐ Cross that bridge later.
☐ One day at a time.
☐ You can always get it fixed.
☐ Don't sweat the small stuff.
☐ Not over 'til the fat lady sings.
☐ It's all nonsense anyway.
☐ You gotta believe in you.
☐ I believe in you.
☐ Anything is possible.
☐ You reacted with integrity.
☐ You can sell it online.
☐ Don't get mad, get even.
☐ No one can tell it's a knockoff.
☐ Just say no.
☐ Hang in there, baby.
☐ If it's not one thing, it's another.
☐ It'll build character.
☐ It was meant to be.
☐ It wasn't meant to be.
☐ If it's meant to be, it'll happen.
☐ Keep your chin up.
☐ You don't need their approval.
☐ For every hill there's a valley.
☐ I would've done the same.
☐ Life goes on.
☐ Absence makes love stronger.
☐ Can't beat 'em? Join 'em.
☐ Shake it off.
☐ No one heard it.
☐ Better late than never.
☐ Better safe than sorry.
☐ And so it goes.
☐ The first cut is the deepest.
☐ Love hurts.
☐ Love stinks.
☐ Love is overrated.
☐ Soon this'll be a distant memory.
☐ Keep on truckin'.
☐ Quit worrying.
☐ It's water under the bridge.
☐ Don't dwell on it.

☐ Ya gotta do what ya gotta do.
☐ When it rains, it pours.
☐ Every rose has a thorn.
☐ You gave it your best shot.
☐ There, there.
☐ It takes all kinds.
☐ They're just jealous.
☐ It'll come when you're ready.
☐ Nobody mentioned it.
☐ Try to keep it in perspective.
☐ Put on your big girl panties.
☐ Put on your big boy briefs.
☐ There's a lid for every pot.
☐ He's probably out of town.
☐ Her phone is probably dead.
☐ You're better off.
☐ It happens sometimes.
☐ They don't understand you.
☐ It was an honest mistake.
☐ Money can't buy love.
☐ Adversity forges character.
☐ You'll feel better after a bath.
☐ You'll feel better after a drink.
☐ It'll make great memoir material.
☐ Quit blaming yourself.
☐ There's no such thing as normal.
☐ You'll show them.
☐ This will forge your character.
☐ You're a superstar.
☐ Just explain what happened.
☐ Don't compare.
☐ All parents screw up.
☐ All kids screw up.
☐ At least you have your health.
☐ He'll grow out of it.
☐ She'll grow out of it.
☐ Shhh. Shhh. It's okay now.
☐ Pain is temporary.
☐ I agree with you.
☐ One day you'll know why.
☐ You march to your own beat.
☐ Ignore what others think.
☐ Buck up, buckwheat.
☐ Everyone sympathizes.
☐ You're overthinking this.
☐ Get back up on the horse.
☐ Just give it some time.
☐ It's not the end of the world.
☐ It gets better.
☐ Really, it is.

☐ **TOTALLY OKAY** ☐ **PRETTY OKAY** ☐ **OKAY-ISH**

SIGNATURE MONTH DAY YEAR

"OKAY? OKAY. OKAY!"

IT'S GONNA BE OKAY

☐ **RIGHT NOW** ☐ **FAIRLY SOON** ☐ **EVENTUALLY**

☐ It'll grow back.
☐ You'll get over it.
☐ You can do this.
☐ It wasn't that obvious.
☐ This too shall pass.
☐ You're too good for him.
☐ You're too good for her.
☐ I'll never tell.
☐ Don't blame yourself.
☐ There are other fish in the sea.
☐ Tattoo removal is easier now.
☐ You are not your job.
☐ Your mother will never know.
☐ Nothing therapy won't cure.
☐ Just take a mulligan.
☐ Moving home is no big deal.
☐ Don't "should" all over yourself.
☐ At least you know you're right.
☐ You did your best.
☐ Can't win 'em all.
☐ You couldn't have known.
☐ My cousin had that and was fine.
☐ Laughter is the best medicine.
☐ Have faith.
☐ Penicillin clears that up fast.
☐ He wasn't thinking.
☐ She wasn't thinking.
☐ If at first you don't succeed . . .
☐ It's about quality, not quantity.
☐ That's not old, it's vintage.
☐ You're not old, you're vintage.
☐ Things happen for a reason.
☐ It'll look better in the morning.
☐ You can blog about it.
☐ We'll look back later and laugh.
☐ No one will ever know.
☐ Here's a hug.
☐ They don't deserve you.
☐ Every cloud has a silver lining.
☐ It was totally his fault.
☐ It was totally her fault.
☐ A rising tide lifts all boats.
☐ There are specialists for that.
☐ Think of the big picture.
☐ Don't let it bother you so much.
☐ No one saw you trip.
☐ You'll get that promotion soon.
☐ It could've been much worse.
☐ Aim for the stars.
☐ You'll forget about it, I promise.

☐ All publicity is good publicity.
☐ You can always return it.
☐ That was so understandable.
☐ You look great.
☐ You look great for your age.
☐ That happens to everyone.
☐ You made your point.
☐ Who wants that responsibility?
☐ It's not more than you can handle.
☐ Time heals all wounds.
☐ Time wounds all heels.
☐ I'm sure you don't normally do that.
☐ Success or not, you are loved.
☐ It's a journey, not a destination.
☐ It was a long shot anyway.
☐ Lesson learned.
☐ It's not you, it's the economy.
☐ You can always sue.
☐ You're the bigger person.
☐ You still have your honor.
☐ You still have your hair.
☐ Heartbreak makes you wiser.
☐ People will see through that.
☐ You'll be the last one standing.
☐ Don't let it get you down.
☐ It's not forever.
☐ There are always people like that.
☐ Never fear, karma's a bitch.
☐ I think it looks cute.
☐ One door closes, another opens.
☐ It's all part of the plan.
☐ Go ahead, cry it out.
☐ They spelled your name right.
☐ Jobs come, jobs go.
☐ People come, people go.
☐ This must be hard for you.
☐ Time to get on with your life.
☐ Everyone's a critic.
☐ It's for the best.
☐ Don't go there.
☐ It's their loss.
☐ You can focus on your career.
☐ You can focus on your kids.
☐ Didn't kill ya; made ya stronger.
☐ Ours is not to reason why.
☐ Don't take it home with you.
☐ Timing is everything.
☐ You'll eventually love it.
☐ Think positive.
☐ Think denial.

☐ Someday you'll understand.
☐ Single life is actually better.
☐ Always darkest before the dawn.
☐ Just clear the browser history.
☐ You're still young.
☐ He isn't worth it.
☐ She isn't worth it.
☐ Where there's a will . . .
☐ Chalk it up to experience.
☐ Cross that bridge later.
☐ One day at a time.
☐ You can always get it fixed.
☐ Don't sweat the small stuff.
☐ Not over 'til the fat lady sings.
☐ It's all nonsense anyway.
☐ You gotta believe in you.
☐ I believe in you.
☐ Anything is possible.
☐ You reacted with integrity.
☐ You can sell it online.
☐ Don't get mad, get even.
☐ No one can tell it's a knockoff.
☐ Just say no.
☐ Hang in there, baby.
☐ If it's not one thing, it's another.
☐ It'll build character.
☐ It was meant to be.
☐ It wasn't meant to be.
☐ If it's meant to be, it'll happen.
☐ Keep your chin up.
☐ You don't need their approval.
☐ For every hill there's a valley.
☐ I would've done the same.
☐ Life goes on.
☐ Absence makes love stronger.
☐ Can't beat 'em? Join 'em.
☐ Shake it off.
☐ No one heard it.
☐ Better late than never.
☐ Better safe than sorry.
☐ And so it goes.
☐ The first cut is the deepest.
☐ Love hurts.
☐ Love stinks.
☐ Love is overrated.
☐ Soon this'll be a distant memory.
☐ Keep on truckin'.
☐ Quit worrying.
☐ It's water under the bridge.
☐ Don't dwell on it.

☐ Ya gotta do what ya gotta do.
☐ When it rains, it pours.
☐ Every rose has a thorn.
☐ You gave it your best shot.
☐ There, there.
☐ It takes all kinds.
☐ They're just jealous.
☐ It'll come when you're ready.
☐ Nobody mentioned it.
☐ Try to keep it in perspective.
☐ Put on your big girl panties.
☐ Put on your big boy briefs.
☐ There's a lid for every pot.
☐ He's probably out of town.
☐ Her phone is probably dead.
☐ You're better off.
☐ It happens sometimes.
☐ They don't understand you.
☐ It was an honest mistake.
☐ Money can't buy love.
☐ Adversity forges character.
☐ You'll feel better after a bath.
☐ You'll feel better after a drink.
☐ It'll make great memoir material.
☐ Quit blaming yourself.
☐ There's no such thing as normal.
☐ You'll show them.
☐ This will forge your character.
☐ You're a superstar.
☐ Just explain what happened.
☐ Don't compare.
☐ All parents screw up.
☐ All kids screw up.
☐ At least you have your health.
☐ He'll grow out of it.
☐ She'll grow out of it.
☐ Shhh. Shhh. It's okay now.
☐ Pain is temporary.
☐ I agree with you.
☐ One day you'll know why.
☐ You march to your own beat.
☐ Ignore what others think.
☐ Buck up, buckwheat.
☐ Everyone sympathizes.
☐ You're overthinking this.
☐ Get back up on the horse.
☐ Just give it some time.
☐ It's not the end of the world.
☐ It gets better.
☐ Really, it is.

☐ **TOTALLY OKAY** ☐ **PRETTY OKAY** ☐ **OKAY-ISH**

SIGNATURE MONTH DAY YEAR

"OKAY? OKAY. OKAY!"

IT'S GONNA BE OKAY

☐ **RIGHT NOW** ☐ **FAIRLY SOON** ☐ **EVENTUALLY**

- ☐ It'll grow back.
- ☐ You'll get over it.
- ☐ You can do this.
- ☐ It wasn't that obvious.
- ☐ This too shall pass.
- ☐ You're too good for him.
- ☐ You're too good for her.
- ☐ I'll never tell.
- ☐ Don't blame yourself.
- ☐ There are other fish in the sea.
- ☐ Tattoo removal is easier now.
- ☐ You are not your job.
- ☐ Your mother will never know.
- ☐ Nothing therapy won't cure.
- ☐ Just take a mulligan.
- ☐ Moving home is no big deal.
- ☐ Don't "should" all over yourself.
- ☐ At least you know you're right.
- ☐ You did your best.
- ☐ Can't win 'em all.
- ☐ You couldn't have known.
- ☐ My cousin had that and was fine.
- ☐ Laughter is the best medicine.
- ☐ Have faith.
- ☐ Penicillin clears that up fast.
- ☐ He wasn't thinking.
- ☐ She wasn't thinking.
- ☐ If at first you don't succeed . . .
- ☐ It's about quality, not quantity.
- ☐ That's not old, it's vintage.
- ☐ You're not old, you're vintage.
- ☐ Things happen for a reason.
- ☐ It'll look better in the morning.
- ☐ You can blog about it.
- ☐ We'll look back later and laugh.
- ☐ No one will ever know.
- ☐ Here's a hug.
- ☐ They don't deserve you.
- ☐ Every cloud has a silver lining.
- ☐ It was totally his fault.
- ☐ It was totally her fault.
- ☐ A rising tide lifts all boats.
- ☐ There are specialists for that.
- ☐ Think of the big picture.
- ☐ Don't let it bother you so much.
- ☐ No one saw you trip.
- ☐ You'll get that promotion soon.
- ☐ It could've been much worse.
- ☐ Aim for the stars.
- ☐ You'll forget about it, I promise.
- ☐ All publicity is good publicity.
- ☐ You can always return it.
- ☐ That was so understandable.
- ☐ You look great.
- ☐ You look great for your age.
- ☐ That happens to everyone.
- ☐ You made your point.
- ☐ Who wants that responsibility?
- ☐ It's not more than you can handle.
- ☐ Time heals all wounds.
- ☐ Time wounds all heels.
- ☐ I'm sure you don't normally do that.
- ☐ Success or not, you are loved.
- ☐ It's a journey, not a destination.
- ☐ It was a long shot anyway.
- ☐ Lesson learned.
- ☐ It's not you, it's the economy.
- ☐ You can always sue.
- ☐ You're the bigger person.
- ☐ You still have your honor.
- ☐ You still have your hair.
- ☐ Heartbreak makes you wiser.
- ☐ People will see through that.
- ☐ You'll be the last one standing.
- ☐ Don't let it get you down.
- ☐ It's not forever.
- ☐ There are always people like that.
- ☐ Never fear, karma's a bitch.
- ☐ I think it looks cute.
- ☐ One door closes, another opens.
- ☐ It's all part of the plan.
- ☐ Go ahead, cry it out.
- ☐ They spelled your name right.
- ☐ Jobs come, jobs go.
- ☐ People come, people go.
- ☐ This must be hard for you.
- ☐ Time to get on with your life.
- ☐ Everyone's a critic.
- ☐ It's for the best.
- ☐ Don't go there.
- ☐ It's their loss.
- ☐ You can focus on your career.
- ☐ You can focus on your kids.
- ☐ Didn't kill ya; made ya stronger.
- ☐ Ours is not to reason why.
- ☐ Don't take it home with you.
- ☐ Timing is everything.
- ☐ You'll eventually love it.
- ☐ Think positive.
- ☐ Think denial.
- ☐ Someday you'll understand.
- ☐ Single life is actually better.
- ☐ Always darkest before the dawn.
- ☐ Just clear the browser history.
- ☐ You're still young.
- ☐ He isn't worth it.
- ☐ She isn't worth it.
- ☐ Where there's a will . . .
- ☐ Chalk it up to experience.
- ☐ Cross that bridge later.
- ☐ One day at a time.
- ☐ You can always get it fixed.
- ☐ Don't sweat the small stuff.
- ☐ Not over 'til the fat lady sings.
- ☐ It's all nonsense anyway.
- ☐ You gotta believe in you.
- ☐ I believe in you.
- ☐ Anything is possible.
- ☐ You reacted with integrity.
- ☐ You can sell it online.
- ☐ Don't get mad, get even.
- ☐ No one can tell it's a knockoff.
- ☐ Just say no.
- ☐ Hang in there, baby.
- ☐ If it's not one thing, it's another.
- ☐ It'll build character.
- ☐ It was meant to be.
- ☐ It wasn't meant to be.
- ☐ If it's meant to be, it'll happen.
- ☐ Keep your chin up.
- ☐ You don't need their approval.
- ☐ For every hill there's a valley.
- ☐ I would've done the same.
- ☐ Life goes on.
- ☐ Absence makes love stronger.
- ☐ Can't beat 'em? Join 'em.
- ☐ Shake it off.
- ☐ No one heard it.
- ☐ Better late than never.
- ☐ Better safe than sorry.
- ☐ And so it goes.
- ☐ The first cut is the deepest.
- ☐ Love hurts.
- ☐ Love stinks.
- ☐ Love is overrated.
- ☐ Soon this'll be a distant memory.
- ☐ Keep on truckin'.
- ☐ Quit worrying.
- ☐ It's water under the bridge.
- ☐ Don't dwell on it.
- ☐ Ya gotta do what ya gotta do.
- ☐ When it rains, it pours.
- ☐ Every rose has a thorn.
- ☐ You gave it your best shot.
- ☐ There, there.
- ☐ It takes all kinds.
- ☐ They're just jealous.
- ☐ It'll come when you're ready.
- ☐ Nobody mentioned it.
- ☐ Try to keep it in perspective.
- ☐ Put on your big girl panties.
- ☐ Put on your big boy briefs.
- ☐ There's a lid for every pot.
- ☐ He's probably out of town.
- ☐ Her phone is probably dead.
- ☐ You're better off.
- ☐ It happens sometimes.
- ☐ They don't understand you.
- ☐ It was an honest mistake.
- ☐ Money can't buy love.
- ☐ Adversity forges character.
- ☐ You'll feel better after a bath.
- ☐ You'll feel better after a drink.
- ☐ It'll make great memoir material.
- ☐ Quit blaming yourself.
- ☐ There's no such thing as normal.
- ☐ You'll show them.
- ☐ This will forge your character.
- ☐ You're a superstar.
- ☐ Just explain what happened.
- ☐ Don't compare.
- ☐ All parents screw up.
- ☐ All kids screw up.
- ☐ At least you have your health.
- ☐ He'll grow out of it.
- ☐ She'll grow out of it.
- ☐ Shhh. Shhh. It's okay now.
- ☐ Pain is temporary.
- ☐ I agree with you.
- ☐ One day you'll know why.
- ☐ You march to your own beat.
- ☐ Ignore what others think.
- ☐ Buck up, buckwheat.
- ☐ Everyone sympathizes.
- ☐ You're overthinking this.
- ☐ Get back up on the horse.
- ☐ Just give it some time.
- ☐ It's not the end of the world.
- ☐ It gets better.
- ☐ Really, it is.

☐ **TOTALLY OKAY** ☐ **PRETTY OKAY** ☐ **OKAY-ISH**

SIGNATURE MONTH DAY YEAR

"OKAY? OKAY. OKAY!"

IT'S GONNA BE OKAY

☐ RIGHT NOW ☐ FAIRLY SOON ☐ EVENTUALLY

☐ It'll grow back.
☐ You'll get over it.
☐ You can do this.
☐ It wasn't that obvious.
☐ This too shall pass.
☐ You're too good for him.
☐ You're too good for her.
☐ I'll never tell.
☐ Don't blame yourself.
☐ There are other fish in the sea.
☐ Tattoo removal is easier now.
☐ You are not your job.
☐ Your mother will never know.
☐ Nothing therapy won't cure.
☐ Just take a mulligan.
☐ Moving home is no big deal.
☐ Don't "should" all over yourself.
☐ At least you know you're right.
☐ You did your best.
☐ Can't win 'em all.
☐ You couldn't have known.
☐ My cousin had that and was fine.
☐ Laughter is the best medicine.
☐ Have faith.
☐ Penicillin clears that up fast.
☐ He wasn't thinking.
☐ She wasn't thinking.
☐ If at first you don't succeed . . .
☐ It's about quality, not quantity.
☐ That's not old, it's vintage.
☐ You're not old, you're vintage.
☐ Things happen for a reason.
☐ It'll look better in the morning.
☐ You can blog about it.
☐ We'll look back later and laugh.
☐ No one will ever know.
☐ Here's a hug.
☐ They don't deserve you.
☐ Every cloud has a silver lining.
☐ It was totally his fault.
☐ It was totally her fault.
☐ A rising tide lifts all boats.
☐ There are specialists for that.
☐ Think of the big picture.
☐ Don't let it bother you so much.
☐ No one saw you trip.
☐ You'll get that promotion soon.
☐ It could've been much worse.
☐ Aim for the stars.
☐ You'll forget about it, I promise.

☐ All publicity is good publicity.
☐ You can always return it.
☐ That was so understandable.
☐ You look great.
☐ You look great for your age.
☐ That happens to everyone.
☐ You made your point.
☐ Who wants that responsibility?
☐ It's not more than you can handle.
☐ Time heals all wounds.
☐ Time wounds all heels.
☐ I'm sure you don't normally do that.
☐ Success or not, you are loved.
☐ It's a journey, not a destination.
☐ It was a long shot anyway.
☐ Lesson learned.
☐ It's not you, it's the economy.
☐ You can always sue.
☐ You're the bigger person.
☐ You still have your honor.
☐ You still have your hair.
☐ Heartbreak makes you wiser.
☐ People will see through that.
☐ You'll be the last one standing.
☐ Don't let it get you down.
☐ It's not forever.
☐ There are always people like that.
☐ Never fear, karma's a bitch.
☐ I think it looks cute.
☐ One door closes, another opens.
☐ It's all part of the plan.
☐ Go ahead, cry it out.
☐ They spelled your name right.
☐ Jobs come, jobs go.
☐ People come, people go.
☐ This must be hard for you.
☐ Time to get on with your life.
☐ Everyone's a critic.
☐ It's for the best.
☐ Don't go there.
☐ It's their loss.
☐ You can focus on your career.
☐ You can focus on your kids.
☐ Didn't kill ya; made ya stronger.
☐ Ours is not to reason why.
☐ Don't take it home with you.
☐ Timing is everything.
☐ You'll eventually love it.
☐ Think positive.
☐ Think denial.

☐ Someday you'll understand.
☐ Single life is actually better.
☐ Always darkest before the dawn.
☐ Just clear the browser history.
☐ You're still young.
☐ He isn't worth it.
☐ She isn't worth it.
☐ Where there's a will . . .
☐ Chalk it up to experience.
☐ Cross that bridge later.
☐ One day at a time.
☐ You can always get it fixed.
☐ Don't sweat the small stuff.
☐ Not over 'til the fat lady sings.
☐ It's all nonsense anyway.
☐ You gotta believe in you.
☐ I believe in you.
☐ Anything is possible.
☐ You reacted with integrity.
☐ You can sell it online.
☐ Don't get mad, get even.
☐ No one can tell it's a knockoff.
☐ Just say no.
☐ Hang in there, baby.
☐ If it's not one thing, it's another.
☐ It'll build character.
☐ It was meant to be.
☐ It wasn't meant to be.
☐ If it's meant to be, it'll happen.
☐ Keep your chin up.
☐ You don't need their approval.
☐ For every hill there's a valley.
☐ I would've done the same.
☐ Life goes on.
☐ Absence makes love stronger.
☐ Can't beat 'em? Join 'em.
☐ Shake it off.
☐ No one heard it.
☐ Better late than never.
☐ Better safe than sorry.
☐ And so it goes.
☐ The first cut is the deepest.
☐ Love hurts.
☐ Love stinks.
☐ Love is overrated.
☐ Soon this'll be a distant memory.
☐ Keep on truckin'.
☐ Quit worrying.
☐ It's water under the bridge.
☐ Don't dwell on it.

☐ Ya gotta do what ya gotta do.
☐ When it rains, it pours.
☐ Every rose has a thorn.
☐ You gave it your best shot.
☐ There, there.
☐ It takes all kinds.
☐ They're just jealous.
☐ It'll come when you're ready.
☐ Nobody mentioned it.
☐ Try to keep it in perspective.
☐ Put on your big girl panties.
☐ Put on your big boy briefs.
☐ There's a lid for every pot.
☐ He's probably out of town.
☐ Her phone is probably dead.
☐ You're better off.
☐ It happens sometimes.
☐ They don't understand you.
☐ It was an honest mistake.
☐ Money can't buy love.
☐ Adversity forges character.
☐ You'll feel better after a bath.
☐ You'll feel better after a drink.
☐ It'll make great memoir material.
☐ Quit blaming yourself.
☐ There's no such thing as normal.
☐ You'll show them.
☐ This will forge your character.
☐ You're a superstar.
☐ Just explain what happened.
☐ Don't compare.
☐ All parents screw up.
☐ All kids screw up.
☐ At least you have your health.
☐ He'll grow out of it.
☐ She'll grow out of it.
☐ Shhh. Shhh. It's okay now.
☐ Pain is temporary.
☐ I agree with you.
☐ One day you'll know why.
☐ You march to your own beat.
☐ Ignore what others think.
☐ Buck up, buckwheat.
☐ Everyone sympathizes.
☐ You're overthinking this.
☐ Get back up on the horse.
☐ Just give it some time.
☐ It's not the end of the world.
☐ It gets better.
☐ Really, it is.

☐ TOTALLY OKAY ☐ PRETTY OKAY ☐ OKAY-ISH

SIGNATURE MONTH DAY YEAR

"OKAY? OKAY. OKAY!"

IT'S GONNA BE OKAY

☐ RIGHT NOW ☐ FAIRLY SOON ☐ EVENTUALLY

☐ It'll grow back.
☐ You'll get over it.
☐ You can do this.
☐ It wasn't that obvious.
☐ This too shall pass.
☐ You're too good for him.
☐ You're too good for her.
☐ I'll never tell.
☐ Don't blame yourself.
☐ There are other fish in the sea.
☐ Tattoo removal is easier now.
☐ You are not your job.
☐ Your mother will never know.
☐ Nothing therapy won't cure.
☐ Just take a mulligan.
☐ Moving home is no big deal.
☐ Don't "should" all over yourself.
☐ At least you know you're right.
☐ You did your best.
☐ Can't win 'em all.
☐ You couldn't have known.
☐ My cousin had that and was fine.
☐ Laughter is the best medicine.
☐ Have faith.
☐ Penicillin clears that up fast.
☐ He wasn't thinking.
☐ She wasn't thinking.
☐ If at first you don't succeed . . .
☐ It's about quality, not quantity.
☐ That's not old, it's vintage.
☐ You're not old, you're vintage.
☐ Things happen for a reason.
☐ It'll look better in the morning.
☐ You can blog about it.
☐ We'll look back later and laugh.
☐ No one will ever know.
☐ Here's a hug.
☐ They don't deserve you.
☐ Every cloud has a silver lining.
☐ It was totally his fault.
☐ It was totally her fault.
☐ A rising tide lifts all boats.
☐ There are specialists for that.
☐ Think of the big picture.
☐ Don't let it bother you so much.
☐ No one saw you trip.
☐ You'll get that promotion soon.
☐ It could've been much worse.
☐ Aim for the stars.
☐ You'll forget about it, I promise.

☐ All publicity is good publicity.
☐ You can always return it.
☐ That was so understandable.
☐ You look great.
☐ You look great for your age.
☐ That happens to everyone.
☐ You made your point.
☐ Who wants that responsibility?
☐ It's not more than you can handle.
☐ Time heals all wounds.
☐ Time wounds all heels.
☐ I'm sure you don't normally do that.
☐ Success or not, you are loved.
☐ It's a journey, not a destination.
☐ It was a long shot anyway.
☐ Lesson learned.
☐ It's not you, it's the economy.
☐ You can always sue.
☐ You're the bigger person.
☐ You still have your honor.
☐ You still have your hair.
☐ Heartbreak makes you wiser.
☐ People will see through that.
☐ You'll be the last one standing.
☐ Don't let it get you down.
☐ It's not forever.
☐ There are always people like that.
☐ Never fear, karma's a bitch.
☐ I think it looks cute.
☐ One door closes, another opens.
☐ It's all part of the plan.
☐ Go ahead, cry it out.
☐ They spelled your name right.
☐ Jobs come, jobs go.
☐ People come, people go.
☐ This must be hard for you.
☐ Time to get on with your life.
☐ Everyone's a critic.
☐ It's for the best.
☐ Don't go there.
☐ It's their loss.
☐ You can focus on your career.
☐ You can focus on your kids.
☐ Didn't kill ya; made ya stronger.
☐ Ours is not to reason why.
☐ Don't take it home with you.
☐ Timing is everything.
☐ You'll eventually love it.
☐ Think positive.
☐ Think denial.

☐ Someday you'll understand.
☐ Single life is actually better.
☐ Always darkest before the dawn.
☐ Just clear the browser history.
☐ You're still young.
☐ He isn't worth it.
☐ She isn't worth it.
☐ Where there's a will . . .
☐ Chalk it up to experience.
☐ Cross that bridge later.
☐ One day at a time.
☐ You can always get it fixed.
☐ Don't sweat the small stuff.
☐ Not over 'til the fat lady sings.
☐ It's all nonsense anyway.
☐ You gotta believe in you.
☐ I believe in you.
☐ Anything is possible.
☐ You reacted with integrity.
☐ You can sell it online.
☐ Don't get mad, get even.
☐ No one can tell it's a knockoff.
☐ Just say no.
☐ Hang in there, baby.
☐ If it's not one thing, it's another.
☐ It'll build character.
☐ It was meant to be.
☐ It wasn't meant to be.
☐ If it's meant to be, it'll happen.
☐ Keep your chin up.
☐ You don't need their approval.
☐ For every hill there's a valley.
☐ I would've done the same.
☐ Life goes on.
☐ Absence makes love stronger.
☐ Can't beat 'em? Join 'em.
☐ Shake it off.
☐ No one heard it.
☐ Better late than never.
☐ Better safe than sorry.
☐ And so it goes.
☐ The first cut is the deepest.
☐ Love hurts.
☐ Love stinks.
☐ Love is overrated.
☐ Soon this'll be a distant memory.
☐ Keep on truckin'.
☐ Quit worrying.
☐ It's water under the bridge.
☐ Don't dwell on it.

☐ Ya gotta do what ya gotta do.
☐ When it rains, it pours.
☐ Every rose has a thorn.
☐ You gave it your best shot.
☐ There, there.
☐ It takes all kinds.
☐ They're just jealous.
☐ It'll come when you're ready.
☐ Nobody mentioned it.
☐ Try to keep it in perspective.
☐ Put on your big girl panties.
☐ Put on your big boy briefs.
☐ There's a lid for every pot.
☐ He's probably out of town.
☐ Her phone is probably dead.
☐ You're better off.
☐ It happens sometimes.
☐ They don't understand you.
☐ It was an honest mistake.
☐ Money can't buy love.
☐ Adversity forges character.
☐ You'll feel better after a bath.
☐ You'll feel better after a drink.
☐ It'll make great memoir material.
☐ Quit blaming yourself.
☐ There's no such thing as normal.
☐ You'll show them.
☐ This will forge your character.
☐ You're a superstar.
☐ Just explain what happened.
☐ Don't compare.
☐ All parents screw up.
☐ All kids screw up.
☐ At least you have your health.
☐ He'll grow out of it.
☐ She'll grow out of it.
☐ Shhh. Shhh. It's okay now.
☐ Pain is temporary.
☐ I agree with you.
☐ One day you'll know why.
☐ You march to your own beat.
☐ Ignore what others think.
☐ Buck up, buckwheat.
☐ Everyone sympathizes.
☐ You're overthinking this.
☐ Get back up on the horse.
☐ Just give it some time.
☐ It's not the end of the world.
☐ It gets better.
☐ Really, it is.

☐ TOTALLY OKAY ☐ PRETTY OKAY ☐ OKAY-ISH

SIGNATURE MONTH DAY YEAR

"OKAY? OKAY. OKAY!"

IT'S GONNA BE OKAY

☐ **RIGHT NOW** ☐ **FAIRLY SOON** ☐ **EVENTUALLY**

☐ It'll grow back.
☐ You'll get over it.
☐ You can do this.
☐ It wasn't that obvious.
☐ This too shall pass.
☐ You're too good for him.
☐ You're too good for her.
☐ I'll never tell.
☐ Don't blame yourself.
☐ There are other fish in the sea.
☐ Tattoo removal is easier now.
☐ You are not your job.
☐ Your mother will never know.
☐ Nothing therapy won't cure.
☐ Just take a mulligan.
☐ Moving home is no big deal.
☐ Don't "should" all over yourself.
☐ At least you know you're right.
☐ You did your best.
☐ Can't win 'em all.
☐ You couldn't have known.
☐ My cousin had that and was fine.
☐ Laughter is the best medicine.
☐ Have faith.
☐ Penicillin clears that up fast.
☐ He wasn't thinking.
☐ She wasn't thinking.
☐ If at first you don't succeed . . .
☐ It's about quality, not quantity.
☐ That's not old, it's vintage.
☐ You're not old, you're vintage.
☐ Things happen for a reason.
☐ It'll look better in the morning.
☐ You can blog about it.
☐ We'll look back later and laugh.
☐ No one will ever know.
☐ Here's a hug.
☐ They don't deserve you.
☐ Every cloud has a silver lining.
☐ It was totally his fault.
☐ It was totally her fault.
☐ A rising tide lifts all boats.
☐ There are specialists for that.
☐ Think of the big picture.
☐ Don't let it bother you so much.
☐ No one saw you trip.
☐ You'll get that promotion soon.
☐ It could've been much worse.
☐ Aim for the stars.
☐ You'll forget about it, I promise.

☐ All publicity is good publicity.
☐ You can always return it.
☐ That was so understandable.
☐ You look great.
☐ You look great for your age.
☐ That happens to everyone.
☐ You made your point.
☐ Who wants that responsibility?
☐ It's not more than you can handle.
☐ Time heals all wounds.
☐ Time wounds all heels.
☐ I'm sure you don't normally do that.
☐ Success or not, you are loved.
☐ It's a journey, not a destination.
☐ It was a long shot anyway.
☐ Lesson learned.
☐ It's not you, it's the economy.
☐ You can always sue.
☐ You're the bigger person.
☐ You still have your honor.
☐ You still have your hair.
☐ Heartbreak makes you wiser.
☐ People will see through that.
☐ You'll be the last one standing.
☐ Don't let it get you down.
☐ It's not forever.
☐ There are always people like that.
☐ Never fear, karma's a bitch.
☐ I think it looks cute.
☐ One door closes, another opens.
☐ It's all part of the plan.
☐ Go ahead, cry it out.
☐ They spelled your name right.
☐ Jobs come, jobs go.
☐ People come, people go.
☐ This must be hard for you.
☐ Time to get on with your life.
☐ Everyone's a critic.
☐ It's for the best.
☐ Don't go there.
☐ It's their loss.
☐ You can focus on your career.
☐ You can focus on your kids.
☐ Didn't kill ya; made ya stronger.
☐ Ours is not to reason why.
☐ Don't take it home with you.
☐ Timing is everything.
☐ You'll eventually love it.
☐ Think positive.
☐ Think denial.

☐ Someday you'll understand.
☐ Single life is actually better.
☐ Always darkest before the dawn.
☐ Just clear the browser history.
☐ You're still young.
☐ He isn't worth it.
☐ She isn't worth it.
☐ Where there's a will . . .
☐ Chalk it up to experience.
☐ Cross that bridge later.
☐ One day at a time.
☐ You can always get it fixed.
☐ Don't sweat the small stuff.
☐ Not over 'til the fat lady sings.
☐ It's all nonsense anyway.
☐ You gotta believe in you.
☐ I believe in you.
☐ Anything is possible.
☐ You reacted with integrity.
☐ You can sell it online.
☐ Don't get mad, get even.
☐ No one can tell it's a knockoff.
☐ Just say no.
☐ Hang in there, baby.
☐ If it's not one thing, it's another.
☐ It'll build character.
☐ It was meant to be.
☐ It wasn't meant to be.
☐ If it's meant to be, it'll happen.
☐ Keep your chin up.
☐ You don't need their approval.
☐ For every hill there's a valley.
☐ I would've done the same.
☐ Life goes on.
☐ Absence makes love stronger.
☐ Can't beat 'em? Join 'em.
☐ Shake it off.
☐ No one heard it.
☐ Better late than never.
☐ Better safe than sorry.
☐ And so it goes.
☐ The first cut is the deepest.
☐ Love hurts.
☐ Love stinks.
☐ Love is overrated.
☐ Soon this'll be a distant memory.
☐ Keep on truckin'.
☐ Quit worrying.
☐ It's water under the bridge.
☐ Don't dwell on it.

☐ Ya gotta do what ya gotta do.
☐ When it rains, it pours.
☐ Every rose has a thorn.
☐ You gave it your best shot.
☐ There, there.
☐ It takes all kinds.
☐ They're just jealous.
☐ It'll come when you're ready.
☐ Nobody mentioned it.
☐ Try to keep it in perspective.
☐ Put on your big girl panties.
☐ Put on your big boy briefs.
☐ There's a lid for every pot.
☐ He's probably out of town.
☐ Her phone is probably dead.
☐ You're better off.
☐ It happens sometimes.
☐ They don't understand you.
☐ It was an honest mistake.
☐ Money can't buy love.
☐ Adversity forges character.
☐ You'll feel better after a bath.
☐ You'll feel better after a drink.
☐ It'll make great memoir material.
☐ Quit blaming yourself.
☐ There's no such thing as normal.
☐ You'll show them.
☐ This will forge your character.
☐ You're a superstar.
☐ Just explain what happened.
☐ Don't compare.
☐ All parents screw up.
☐ All kids screw up.
☐ At least you have your health.
☐ He'll grow out of it.
☐ She'll grow out of it.
☐ Shhh. Shhh. It's okay now.
☐ Pain is temporary.
☐ I agree with you.
☐ One day you'll know why.
☐ You march to your own beat.
☐ Ignore what others think.
☐ Buck up, buckwheat.
☐ Everyone sympathizes.
☐ You're overthinking this.
☐ Get back up on the horse.
☐ Just give it some time.
☐ It's not the end of the world.
☐ It gets better.
☐ Really, it is.

☐ **TOTALLY OKAY** ☐ **PRETTY OKAY** ☐ **OKAY-ISH**

SIGNATURE

MONTH : DAY : YEAR

"OKAY? OKAY. OKAY!"

IT'S GONNA BE OKAY

☐ **RIGHT NOW** ☐ **FAIRLY SOON** ☐ **EVENTUALLY**

☐ It'll grow back.
☐ You'll get over it.
☐ You can do this.
☐ It wasn't that obvious.
☐ This too shall pass.
☐ You're too good for him.
☐ You're too good for her.
☐ I'll never tell.
☐ Don't blame yourself.
☐ There are other fish in the sea.
☐ Tattoo removal is easier now.
☐ You are not your job.
☐ Your mother will never know.
☐ Nothing therapy won't cure.
☐ Just take a mulligan.
☐ Moving home is no big deal.
☐ Don't "should" all over yourself.
☐ At least you know you're right.
☐ You did your best.
☐ Can't win 'em all.
☐ You couldn't have known.
☐ My cousin had that and was fine.
☐ Laughter is the best medicine.
☐ Have faith.
☐ Penicillin clears that up fast.
☐ He wasn't thinking.
☐ She wasn't thinking.
☐ If at first you don't succeed . . .
☐ It's about quality, not quantity.
☐ That's not old, it's vintage.
☐ You're not old, you're vintage.
☐ Things happen for a reason.
☐ It'll look better in the morning.
☐ You can blog about it.
☐ We'll look back later and laugh.
☐ No one will ever know.
☐ Here's a hug.
☐ They don't deserve you.
☐ Every cloud has a silver lining.
☐ It was totally his fault.
☐ It was totally her fault.
☐ A rising tide lifts all boats.
☐ There are specialists for that.
☐ Think of the big picture.
☐ Don't let it bother you so much.
☐ No one saw you trip.
☐ You'll get that promotion soon.
☐ It could've been much worse.
☐ Aim for the stars.
☐ You'll forget about it, I promise.

☐ All publicity is good publicity.
☐ You can always return it.
☐ That was so understandable.
☐ You look great.
☐ You look great for your age.
☐ That happens to everyone.
☐ You made your point.
☐ Who wants that responsibility?
☐ It's not more than you can handle.
☐ Time heals all wounds.
☐ Time wounds all heels.
☐ I'm sure you don't normally do that.
☐ Success or not, you are loved.
☐ It's a journey, not a destination.
☐ It was a long shot anyway.
☐ Lesson learned.
☐ It's not you, it's the economy.
☐ You can always sue.
☐ You're the bigger person.
☐ You still have your honor.
☐ You still have your hair.
☐ Heartbreak makes you wiser.
☐ People will see through that.
☐ You'll be the last one standing.
☐ Don't let it get you down.
☐ It's not forever.
☐ There are always people like that.
☐ Never fear, karma's a bitch.
☐ I think it looks cute.
☐ One door closes, another opens.
☐ It's all part of the plan.
☐ Go ahead, cry it out.
☐ They spelled your name right.
☐ Jobs come, jobs go.
☐ People come, people go.
☐ This must be hard for you.
☐ Time to get on with your life.
☐ Everyone's a critic.
☐ It's for the best.
☐ Don't go there.
☐ It's their loss.
☐ You can focus on your career.
☐ You can focus on your kids.
☐ Didn't kill ya; made ya stronger.
☐ Ours is not to reason why.
☐ Don't take it home with you.
☐ Timing is everything.
☐ You'll eventually love it.
☐ Think positive.
☐ Think denial.

☐ Someday you'll understand.
☐ Single life is actually better.
☐ Always darkest before the dawn.
☐ Just clear the browser history.
☐ You're still young.
☐ He isn't worth it.
☐ She isn't worth it.
☐ Where there's a will . . .
☐ Chalk it up to experience.
☐ Cross that bridge later.
☐ One day at a time.
☐ You can always get it fixed.
☐ Don't sweat the small stuff.
☐ Not over 'til the fat lady sings.
☐ It's all nonsense anyway.
☐ You gotta believe in you.
☐ I believe in you.
☐ Anything is possible.
☐ You reacted with integrity.
☐ You can sell it online.
☐ Don't get mad, get even.
☐ No one can tell it's a knockoff.
☐ Just say no.
☐ Hang in there, baby.
☐ If it's not one thing, it's another.
☐ It'll build character.
☐ It was meant to be.
☐ It wasn't meant to be.
☐ If it's meant to be, it'll happen.
☐ Keep your chin up.
☐ You don't need their approval.
☐ For every hill there's a valley.
☐ I would've done the same.
☐ Life goes on.
☐ Absence makes love stronger.
☐ Can't beat 'em? Join 'em.
☐ Shake it off.
☐ No one heard it.
☐ Better late than never.
☐ Better safe than sorry.
☐ And so it goes.
☐ The first cut is the deepest.
☐ Love hurts.
☐ Love stinks.
☐ Love is overrated.
☐ Soon this'll be a distant memory.
☐ Keep on truckin'.
☐ Quit worrying.
☐ It's water under the bridge.
☐ Don't dwell on it.

☐ Ya gotta do what ya gotta do.
☐ When it rains, it pours.
☐ Every rose has a thorn.
☐ You gave it your best shot.
☐ There, there.
☐ It takes all kinds.
☐ They're just jealous.
☐ It'll come when you're ready.
☐ Nobody mentioned it.
☐ Try to keep it in perspective.
☐ Put on your big girl panties.
☐ Put on your big boy briefs.
☐ There's a lid for every pot.
☐ He's probably out of town.
☐ Her phone is probably dead.
☐ You're better off.
☐ It happens sometimes.
☐ They don't understand you.
☐ It was an honest mistake.
☐ Money can't buy love.
☐ Adversity forges character.
☐ You'll feel better after a bath.
☐ You'll feel better after a drink.
☐ It'll make great memoir material.
☐ Quit blaming yourself.
☐ There's no such thing as normal.
☐ You'll show them.
☐ This will forge your character.
☐ You're a superstar.
☐ Just explain what happened.
☐ Don't compare.
☐ All parents screw up.
☐ All kids screw up.
☐ At least you have your health.
☐ He'll grow out of it.
☐ She'll grow out of it.
☐ Shhh. Shhh. It's okay now.
☐ Pain is temporary.
☐ I agree with you.
☐ One day you'll know why.
☐ You march to your own beat.
☐ Ignore what others think.
☐ Buck up, buckwheat.
☐ Everyone sympathizes.
☐ You're overthinking this.
☐ Get back up on the horse.
☐ Just give it some time.
☐ It's not the end of the world.
☐ It gets better.
☐ Really, it is.

☐ **TOTALLY OKAY** ☐ **PRETTY OKAY** ☐ **OKAY-ISH**

SIGNATURE MONTH DAY YEAR

"OKAY? OKAY. OKAY!"

IT'S GONNA BE OKAY

☐ RIGHT NOW ☐ FAIRLY SOON ☐ EVENTUALLY

- ☐ It'll grow back.
- ☐ You'll get over it.
- ☐ You can do this.
- ☐ It wasn't that obvious.
- ☐ This too shall pass.
- ☐ You're too good for him.
- ☐ You're too good for her.
- ☐ I'll never tell.
- ☐ Don't blame yourself.
- ☐ There are other fish in the sea.
- ☐ Tattoo removal is easier now.
- ☐ You are not your job.
- ☐ Your mother will never know.
- ☐ Nothing therapy won't cure.
- ☐ Just take a mulligan.
- ☐ Moving home is no big deal.
- ☐ Don't "should" all over yourself.
- ☐ At least you know you're right.
- ☐ You did your best.
- ☐ Can't win 'em all.
- ☐ You couldn't have known.
- ☐ My cousin had that and was fine.
- ☐ Laughter is the best medicine.
- ☐ Have faith.
- ☐ Penicillin clears that up fast.
- ☐ He wasn't thinking.
- ☐ She wasn't thinking.
- ☐ If at first you don't succeed . . .
- ☐ It's about quality, not quantity.
- ☐ That's not old, it's vintage.
- ☐ You're not old, you're vintage.
- ☐ Things happen for a reason.
- ☐ It'll look better in the morning.
- ☐ You can blog about it.
- ☐ We'll look back later and laugh.
- ☐ No one will ever know.
- ☐ Here's a hug.
- ☐ They don't deserve you.
- ☐ Every cloud has a silver lining.
- ☐ It was totally his fault.
- ☐ It was totally her fault.
- ☐ A rising tide lifts all boats.
- ☐ There are specialists for that.
- ☐ Think of the big picture.
- ☐ Don't let it bother you so much.
- ☐ No one saw you trip.
- ☐ You'll get that promotion soon.
- ☐ It could've been much worse.
- ☐ Aim for the stars.
- ☐ You'll forget about it, I promise.
- ☐ All publicity is good publicity.
- ☐ You can always return it.
- ☐ That was so understandable.
- ☐ You look great.
- ☐ You look great for your age.
- ☐ That happens to everyone.
- ☐ You made your point.
- ☐ Who wants that responsibility?
- ☐ It's not more than you can handle.
- ☐ Time heals all wounds.
- ☐ Time wounds all heels.
- ☐ I'm sure you don't normally do that.
- ☐ Success or not, you are loved.
- ☐ It's a journey, not a destination.
- ☐ It was a long shot anyway.
- ☐ Lesson learned.
- ☐ It's not you, it's the economy.
- ☐ You can always sue.
- ☐ You're the bigger person.
- ☐ You still have your honor.
- ☐ You still have your hair.
- ☐ Heartbreak makes you wiser.
- ☐ People will see through that.
- ☐ You'll be the last one standing.
- ☐ Don't let it get you down.
- ☐ It's not forever.
- ☐ There are always people like that.
- ☐ Never fear, karma's a bitch.
- ☐ I think it looks cute.
- ☐ One door closes, another opens.
- ☐ It's all part of the plan.
- ☐ Go ahead, cry it out.
- ☐ They spelled your name right.
- ☐ Jobs come, jobs go.
- ☐ People come, people go.
- ☐ This must be hard for you.
- ☐ Time to get on with your life.
- ☐ Everyone's a critic.
- ☐ It's for the best.
- ☐ Don't go there.
- ☐ It's their loss.
- ☐ You can focus on your career.
- ☐ You can focus on your kids.
- ☐ Didn't kill ya; made ya stronger.
- ☐ Ours is not to reason why.
- ☐ Don't take it home with you.
- ☐ Timing is everything.
- ☐ You'll eventually love it.
- ☐ Think positive.
- ☐ Think denial.
- ☐ Someday you'll understand.
- ☐ Single life is actually better.
- ☐ Always darkest before the dawn.
- ☐ Just clear the browser history.
- ☐ You're still young.
- ☐ He isn't worth it.
- ☐ She isn't worth it.
- ☐ Where there's a will . . .
- ☐ Chalk it up to experience.
- ☐ Cross that bridge later.
- ☐ One day at a time.
- ☐ You can always get it fixed.
- ☐ Don't sweat the small stuff.
- ☐ Not over 'til the fat lady sings.
- ☐ It's all nonsense anyway.
- ☐ You gotta believe in you.
- ☐ I believe in you.
- ☐ Anything is possible.
- ☐ You reacted with integrity.
- ☐ You can sell it online.
- ☐ Don't get mad, get even.
- ☐ No one can tell it's a knockoff.
- ☐ Just say no.
- ☐ Hang in there, baby.
- ☐ If it's not one thing, it's another.
- ☐ It'll build character.
- ☐ It was meant to be.
- ☐ It wasn't meant to be.
- ☐ If it's meant to be, it'll happen.
- ☐ Keep your chin up.
- ☐ You don't need their approval.
- ☐ For every hill there's a valley.
- ☐ I would've done the same.
- ☐ Life goes on.
- ☐ Absence makes love stronger.
- ☐ Can't beat 'em? Join 'em.
- ☐ Shake it off.
- ☐ No one heard it.
- ☐ Better late than never.
- ☐ Better safe than sorry.
- ☐ And so it goes.
- ☐ The first cut is the deepest.
- ☐ Love hurts.
- ☐ Love stinks.
- ☐ Love is overrated.
- ☐ Soon this'll be a distant memory.
- ☐ Keep on truckin'.
- ☐ Quit worrying.
- ☐ It's water under the bridge.
- ☐ Don't dwell on it.
- ☐ Ya gotta do what ya gotta do.
- ☐ When it rains, it pours.
- ☐ Every rose has a thorn.
- ☐ You gave it your best shot.
- ☐ There, there.
- ☐ It takes all kinds.
- ☐ They're just jealous.
- ☐ It'll come when you're ready.
- ☐ Nobody mentioned it.
- ☐ Try to keep it in perspective.
- ☐ Put on your big girl panties.
- ☐ Put on your big boy briefs.
- ☐ There's a lid for every pot.
- ☐ He's probably out of town.
- ☐ Her phone is probably dead.
- ☐ You're better off.
- ☐ It happens sometimes.
- ☐ They don't understand you.
- ☐ It was an honest mistake.
- ☐ Money can't buy love.
- ☐ Adversity forges character.
- ☐ You'll feel better after a bath.
- ☐ You'll feel better after a drink.
- ☐ It'll make great memoir material.
- ☐ Quit blaming yourself.
- ☐ There's no such thing as normal.
- ☐ You'll show them.
- ☐ This will forge your character.
- ☐ You're a superstar.
- ☐ Just explain what happened.
- ☐ Don't compare.
- ☐ All parents screw up.
- ☐ All kids screw up.
- ☐ At least you have your health.
- ☐ He'll grow out of it.
- ☐ She'll grow out of it.
- ☐ Shhh. Shhh. It's okay now.
- ☐ Pain is temporary.
- ☐ I agree with you.
- ☐ One day you'll know why.
- ☐ You march to your own beat.
- ☐ Ignore what others think.
- ☐ Buck up, buckwheat.
- ☐ Everyone sympathizes.
- ☐ You're overthinking this.
- ☐ Get back up on the horse.
- ☐ Just give it some time.
- ☐ It's not the end of the world.
- ☐ It gets better.
- ☐ Really, it is.

☐ TOTALLY OKAY ☐ PRETTY OKAY ☐ OKAY-ISH

SIGNATURE	MONTH	DAY	YEAR

"OKAY? OKAY. OKAY!"

IT'S GONNA BE OKAY

☐ RIGHT NOW ☐ FAIRLY SOON ☐ EVENTUALLY

☐ It'll grow back.
☐ You'll get over it.
☐ You can do this.
☐ It wasn't that obvious.
☐ This too shall pass.
☐ You're too good for him.
☐ You're too good for her.
☐ I'll never tell.
☐ Don't blame yourself.
☐ There are other fish in the sea.
☐ Tattoo removal is easier now.
☐ You are not your job.
☐ Your mother will never know.
☐ Nothing therapy won't cure.
☐ Just take a mulligan.
☐ Moving home is no big deal.
☐ Don't "should" all over yourself.
☐ At least you know you're right.
☐ You did your best.
☐ Can't win 'em all.
☐ You couldn't have known.
☐ My cousin had that and was fine.
☐ Laughter is the best medicine.
☐ Have faith.
☐ Penicillin clears that up fast.
☐ He wasn't thinking.
☐ She wasn't thinking.
☐ If at first you don't succeed . . .
☐ It's about quality, not quantity.
☐ That's not old, it's vintage.
☐ You're not old, you're vintage.
☐ Things happen for a reason.
☐ It'll look better in the morning.
☐ You can blog about it.
☐ We'll look back later and laugh.
☐ No one will ever know.
☐ Here's a hug.
☐ They don't deserve you.
☐ Every cloud has a silver lining.
☐ It was totally his fault.
☐ It was totally her fault.
☐ A rising tide lifts all boats.
☐ There are specialists for that.
☐ Think of the big picture.
☐ Don't let it bother you so much.
☐ No one saw you trip.
☐ You'll get that promotion soon.
☐ It could've been much worse.
☐ Aim for the stars.
☐ You'll forget about it, I promise.

☐ All publicity is good publicity.
☐ You can always return it.
☐ That was so understandable.
☐ You look great.
☐ You look great for your age.
☐ That happens to everyone.
☐ You made your point.
☐ Who wants that responsibility?
☐ It's not more than you can handle.
☐ Time heals all wounds.
☐ Time wounds all heels.
☐ I'm sure you don't normally do that.
☐ Success or not, you are loved.
☐ It's a journey, not a destination.
☐ It was a long shot anyway.
☐ Lesson learned.
☐ It's not you, it's the economy.
☐ You can always sue.
☐ You're the bigger person.
☐ You still have your honor.
☐ You still have your hair.
☐ Heartbreak makes you wiser.
☐ People will see through that.
☐ You'll be the last one standing.
☐ Don't let it get you down.
☐ It's not forever.
☐ There are always people like that.
☐ Never fear, karma's a bitch.
☐ I think it looks cute.
☐ One door closes, another opens.
☐ It's all part of the plan.
☐ Go ahead, cry it out.
☐ They spelled your name right.
☐ Jobs come, jobs go.
☐ People come, people go.
☐ This must be hard for you.
☐ Time to get on with your life.
☐ Everyone's a critic.
☐ It's for the best.
☐ Don't go there.
☐ It's their loss.
☐ You can focus on your career.
☐ You can focus on your kids.
☐ Didn't kill ya; made ya stronger.
☐ Ours is not to reason why.
☐ Don't take it home with you.
☐ Timing is everything.
☐ You'll eventually love it.
☐ Think positive.
☐ Think denial.

☐ Someday you'll understand.
☐ Single life is actually better.
☐ Always darkest before the dawn.
☐ Just clear the browser history.
☐ You're still young.
☐ He isn't worth it.
☐ She isn't worth it.
☐ Where there's a will . . .
☐ Chalk it up to experience.
☐ Cross that bridge later.
☐ One day at a time.
☐ You can always get it fixed.
☐ Don't sweat the small stuff.
☐ Not over 'til the fat lady sings.
☐ It's all nonsense anyway.
☐ You gotta believe in you.
☐ I believe in you.
☐ Anything is possible.
☐ You reacted with integrity.
☐ You can sell it online.
☐ Don't get mad, get even.
☐ No one can tell it's a knockoff.
☐ Just say no.
☐ Hang in there, baby.
☐ If it's not one thing, it's another.
☐ It'll build character.
☐ It was meant to be.
☐ It wasn't meant to be.
☐ If it's meant to be, it'll happen.
☐ Keep your chin up.
☐ You don't need their approval.
☐ For every hill there's a valley.
☐ I would've done the same.
☐ Life goes on.
☐ Absence makes love stronger.
☐ Can't beat 'em? Join 'em.
☐ Shake it off.
☐ No one heard it.
☐ Better late than never.
☐ Better safe than sorry.
☐ And so it goes.
☐ The first cut is the deepest.
☐ Love hurts.
☐ Love stinks.
☐ Love is overrated.
☐ Soon this'll be a distant memory.
☐ Keep on truckin'.
☐ Quit worrying.
☐ It's water under the bridge.
☐ Don't dwell on it.

☐ Ya gotta do what ya gotta do.
☐ When it rains, it pours.
☐ Every rose has a thorn.
☐ You gave it your best shot.
☐ There, there.
☐ It takes all kinds.
☐ They're just jealous.
☐ It'll come when you're ready.
☐ Nobody mentioned it.
☐ Try to keep it in perspective.
☐ Put on your big girl panties.
☐ Put on your big boy briefs.
☐ There's a lid for every pot.
☐ He's probably out of town.
☐ Her phone is probably dead.
☐ You're better off.
☐ It happens sometimes.
☐ They don't understand you.
☐ It was an honest mistake.
☐ Money can't buy love.
☐ Adversity forges character.
☐ You'll feel better after a bath.
☐ You'll feel better after a drink.
☐ It'll make great memoir material.
☐ Quit blaming yourself.
☐ There's no such thing as normal.
☐ You'll show them.
☐ This will forge your character.
☐ You're a superstar.
☐ Just explain what happened.
☐ Don't compare.
☐ All parents screw up.
☐ All kids screw up.
☐ At least you have your health.
☐ He'll grow out of it.
☐ She'll grow out of it.
☐ Shhh. Shhh. It's okay now.
☐ Pain is temporary.
☐ I agree with you.
☐ One day you'll know why.
☐ You march to your own beat.
☐ Ignore what others think.
☐ Buck up, buckwheat.
☐ Everyone sympathizes.
☐ You're overthinking this.
☐ Get back up on the horse.
☐ Just give it some time.
☐ It's not the end of the world.
☐ It gets better.
☐ Really, it is.

☐ TOTALLY OKAY ☐ PRETTY OKAY ☐ OKAY-ISH

SIGNATURE

MONTH : DAY : YEAR

"OKAY? OKAY. OKAY!"

IT'S GONNA BE OKAY

☐ **RIGHT NOW** ☐ **FAIRLY SOON** ☐ **EVENTUALLY**

☐ It'll grow back.
☐ You'll get over it.
☐ You can do this.
☐ It wasn't that obvious.
☐ This too shall pass.
☐ You're too good for him.
☐ You're too good for her.
☐ I'll never tell.
☐ Don't blame yourself.
☐ There are other fish in the sea.
☐ Tattoo removal is easier now.
☐ You are not your job.
☐ Your mother will never know.
☐ Nothing therapy won't cure.
☐ Just take a mulligan.
☐ Moving home is no big deal.
☐ Don't "should" all over yourself.
☐ At least you know you're right.
☐ You did your best.
☐ Can't win 'em all.
☐ You couldn't have known.
☐ My cousin had that and was fine.
☐ Laughter is the best medicine.
☐ Have faith.
☐ Penicillin clears that up fast.
☐ He wasn't thinking.
☐ She wasn't thinking.
☐ If at first you don't succeed . . .
☐ It's about quality, not quantity.
☐ That's not old, it's vintage.
☐ You're not old, you're vintage.
☐ Things happen for a reason.
☐ It'll look better in the morning.
☐ You can blog about it.
☐ We'll look back later and laugh.
☐ No one will ever know.
☐ Here's a hug.
☐ They don't deserve you.
☐ Every cloud has a silver lining.
☐ It was totally his fault.
☐ It was totally her fault.
☐ A rising tide lifts all boats.
☐ There are specialists for that.
☐ Think of the big picture.
☐ Don't let it bother you so much.
☐ No one saw you trip.
☐ You'll get that promotion soon.
☐ It could've been much worse.
☐ Aim for the stars.
☐ You'll forget about it, I promise.

☐ All publicity is good publicity.
☐ You can always return it.
☐ That was so understandable.
☐ You look great.
☐ You look great for your age.
☐ That happens to everyone.
☐ You made your point.
☐ Who wants that responsibility?
☐ It's not more than you can handle.
☐ Time heals all wounds.
☐ Time wounds all heels.
☐ I'm sure you don't normally do that.
☐ Success or not, you are loved.
☐ It's a journey, not a destination.
☐ It was a long shot anyway.
☐ Lesson learned.
☐ It's not you, it's the economy.
☐ You can always sue.
☐ You're the bigger person.
☐ You still have your honor.
☐ You still have your hair.
☐ Heartbreak makes you wiser.
☐ People will see through that.
☐ You'll be the last one standing.
☐ Don't let it get you down.
☐ It's not forever.
☐ There are always people like that.
☐ Never fear, karma's a bitch.
☐ I think it looks cute.
☐ One door closes, another opens.
☐ It's all part of the plan.
☐ Go ahead, cry it out.
☐ They spelled your name right.
☐ Jobs come, jobs go.
☐ People come, people go.
☐ This must be hard for you.
☐ Time to get on with your life.
☐ Everyone's a critic.
☐ It's for the best.
☐ Don't go there.
☐ It's their loss.
☐ You can focus on your career.
☐ You can focus on your kids.
☐ Didn't kill ya; made ya stronger.
☐ Ours is not to reason why.
☐ Don't take it home with you.
☐ Timing is everything.
☐ You'll eventually love it.
☐ Think positive.
☐ Think denial.

☐ Someday you'll understand.
☐ Single life is actually better.
☐ Always darkest before the dawn.
☐ Just clear the browser history.
☐ You're still young.
☐ He isn't worth it.
☐ She isn't worth it.
☐ Where there's a will . . .
☐ Chalk it up to experience.
☐ Cross that bridge later.
☐ One day at a time.
☐ You can always get it fixed.
☐ Don't sweat the small stuff.
☐ Not over 'til the fat lady sings.
☐ It's all nonsense anyway.
☐ You gotta believe in you.
☐ I believe in you.
☐ Anything is possible.
☐ You reacted with integrity.
☐ You can sell it online.
☐ Don't get mad, get even.
☐ No one can tell it's a knockoff.
☐ Just say no.
☐ Hang in there, baby.
☐ If it's not one thing, it's another.
☐ It'll build character.
☐ It was meant to be.
☐ It wasn't meant to be.
☐ If it's meant to be, it'll happen.
☐ Keep your chin up.
☐ You don't need their approval.
☐ For every hill there's a valley.
☐ I would've done the same.
☐ Life goes on.
☐ Absence makes love stronger.
☐ Can't beat 'em? Join 'em.
☐ Shake it off.
☐ No one heard it.
☐ Better late than never.
☐ Better safe than sorry.
☐ And so it goes.
☐ The first cut is the deepest.
☐ Love hurts.
☐ Love stinks.
☐ Love is overrated.
☐ Soon this'll be a distant memory.
☐ Keep on truckin'.
☐ Quit worrying.
☐ It's water under the bridge.
☐ Don't dwell on it.

☐ Ya gotta do what ya gotta do.
☐ When it rains, it pours.
☐ Every rose has a thorn.
☐ You gave it your best shot.
☐ There, there.
☐ It takes all kinds.
☐ They're just jealous.
☐ It'll come when you're ready.
☐ Nobody mentioned it.
☐ Try to keep it in perspective.
☐ Put on your big girl panties.
☐ Put on your big boy briefs.
☐ There's a lid for every pot.
☐ He's probably out of town.
☐ Her phone is probably dead.
☐ You're better off.
☐ It happens sometimes.
☐ They don't understand you.
☐ It was an honest mistake.
☐ Money can't buy love.
☐ Adversity forges character.
☐ You'll feel better after a bath.
☐ You'll feel better after a drink.
☐ It'll make great memoir material.
☐ Quit blaming yourself.
☐ There's no such thing as normal.
☐ You'll show them.
☐ This will forge your character.
☐ You're a superstar.
☐ Just explain what happened.
☐ Don't compare.
☐ All parents screw up.
☐ All kids screw up.
☐ At least you have your health.
☐ He'll grow out of it.
☐ She'll grow out of it.
☐ Shhh. Shhh. It's okay now.
☐ Pain is temporary.
☐ I agree with you.
☐ One day you'll know why.
☐ You march to your own beat.
☐ Ignore what others think.
☐ Buck up, buckwheat.
☐ Everyone sympathizes.
☐ You're overthinking this.
☐ Get back up on the horse.
☐ Just give it some time.
☐ It's not the end of the world.
☐ It gets better.
☐ Really, it is.

☐ **TOTALLY OKAY** ☐ **PRETTY OKAY** ☐ **OKAY-ISH**

SIGNATURE MONTH DAY YEAR

"OKAY? OKAY. OKAY!"

IT'S GONNA BE OKAY

☐ **RIGHT NOW** ☐ **FAIRLY SOON** ☐ **EVENTUALLY**

☐ It'll grow back.
☐ You'll get over it.
☐ You can do this.
☐ It wasn't that obvious.
☐ This too shall pass.
☐ You're too good for him.
☐ You're too good for her.
☐ I'll never tell.
☐ Don't blame yourself.
☐ There are other fish in the sea.
☐ Tattoo removal is easier now.
☐ You are not your job.
☐ Your mother will never know.
☐ Nothing therapy won't cure.
☐ Just take a mulligan.
☐ Moving home is no big deal.
☐ Don't "should" all over yourself.
☐ At least you know you're right.
☐ You did your best.
☐ Can't win 'em all.
☐ You couldn't have known.
☐ My cousin had that and was fine.
☐ Laughter is the best medicine.
☐ Have faith.
☐ Penicillin clears that up fast.
☐ He wasn't thinking.
☐ She wasn't thinking.
☐ If at first you don't succeed . . .
☐ It's about quality, not quantity.
☐ That's not old, it's vintage.
☐ You're not old, you're vintage.
☐ Things happen for a reason.
☐ It'll look better in the morning.
☐ You can blog about it.
☐ We'll look back later and laugh.
☐ No one will ever know.
☐ Here's a hug.
☐ They don't deserve you.
☐ Every cloud has a silver lining.
☐ It was totally his fault.
☐ It was totally her fault.
☐ A rising tide lifts all boats.
☐ There are specialists for that.
☐ Think of the big picture.
☐ Don't let it bother you so much.
☐ No one saw you trip.
☐ You'll get that promotion soon.
☐ It could've been much worse.
☐ Aim for the stars.
☐ You'll forget about it, I promise.

☐ All publicity is good publicity.
☐ You can always return it.
☐ That was so understandable.
☐ You look great.
☐ You look great for your age.
☐ That happens to everyone.
☐ You made your point.
☐ Who wants that responsibility?
☐ It's not more than you can handle.
☐ Time heals all wounds.
☐ Time wounds all heels.
☐ I'm sure you don't normally do that.
☐ Success or not, you are loved.
☐ It's a journey, not a destination.
☐ It was a long shot anyway.
☐ Lesson learned.
☐ It's not you, it's the economy.
☐ You can always sue.
☐ You're the bigger person.
☐ You still have your honor.
☐ You still have your hair.
☐ Heartbreak makes you wiser.
☐ People will see through that.
☐ You'll be the last one standing.
☐ Don't let it get you down.
☐ It's not forever.
☐ There are always people like that.
☐ Never fear, karma's a bitch.
☐ I think it looks cute.
☐ One door closes, another opens.
☐ It's all part of the plan.
☐ Go ahead, cry it out.
☐ They spelled your name right.
☐ Jobs come, jobs go.
☐ People come, people go.
☐ This must be hard for you.
☐ Time to get on with your life.
☐ Everyone's a critic.
☐ It's for the best.
☐ Don't go there.
☐ It's their loss.
☐ You can focus on your career.
☐ You can focus on your kids.
☐ Didn't kill ya; made ya stronger.
☐ Ours is not to reason why.
☐ Don't take it home with you.
☐ Timing is everything.
☐ You'll eventually love it.
☐ Think positive.
☐ Think denial.

☐ Someday you'll understand.
☐ Single life is actually better.
☐ Always darkest before the dawn.
☐ Just clear the browser history.
☐ You're still young.
☐ He isn't worth it.
☐ She isn't worth it.
☐ Where there's a will . . .
☐ Chalk it up to experience.
☐ Cross that bridge later.
☐ One day at a time.
☐ You can always get it fixed.
☐ Don't sweat the small stuff.
☐ Not over 'til the fat lady sings.
☐ It's all nonsense anyway.
☐ You gotta believe in you.
☐ I believe in you.
☐ Anything is possible.
☐ You reacted with integrity.
☐ You can sell it online.
☐ Don't get mad, get even.
☐ No one can tell it's a knockoff.
☐ Just say no.
☐ Hang in there, baby.
☐ If it's not one thing, it's another.
☐ It'll build character.
☐ It was meant to be.
☐ It wasn't meant to be.
☐ If it's meant to be, it'll happen.
☐ Keep your chin up.
☐ You don't need their approval.
☐ For every hill there's a valley.
☐ I would've done the same.
☐ Life goes on.
☐ Absence makes love stronger.
☐ Can't beat 'em? Join 'em.
☐ Shake it off.
☐ No one heard it.
☐ Better late than never.
☐ Better safe than sorry.
☐ And so it goes.
☐ The first cut is the deepest.
☐ Love hurts.
☐ Love stinks.
☐ Love is overrated.
☐ Soon this'll be a distant memory.
☐ Keep on truckin'.
☐ Quit worrying.
☐ It's water under the bridge.
☐ Don't dwell on it.

☐ Ya gotta do what ya gotta do.
☐ When it rains, it pours.
☐ Every rose has a thorn.
☐ You gave it your best shot.
☐ There, there.
☐ It takes all kinds.
☐ They're just jealous.
☐ It'll come when you're ready.
☐ Nobody mentioned it.
☐ Try to keep it in perspective.
☐ Put on your big girl panties.
☐ Put on your big boy briefs.
☐ There's a lid for every pot.
☐ He's probably out of town.
☐ Her phone is probably dead.
☐ You're better off.
☐ It happens sometimes.
☐ They don't understand you.
☐ It was an honest mistake.
☐ Money can't buy love.
☐ Adversity forges character.
☐ You'll feel better after a bath.
☐ You'll feel better after a drink.
☐ It'll make great memoir material.
☐ Quit blaming yourself.
☐ There's no such thing as normal.
☐ You'll show them.
☐ This will forge your character.
☐ You're a superstar.
☐ Just explain what happened.
☐ Don't compare.
☐ All parents screw up.
☐ All kids screw up.
☐ At least you have your health.
☐ He'll grow out of it.
☐ She'll grow out of it.
☐ Shhh. Shhh. It's okay now.
☐ Pain is temporary.
☐ I agree with you.
☐ One day you'll know why.
☐ You march to your own beat.
☐ Ignore what others think.
☐ Buck up, buckwheat.
☐ Everyone sympathizes.
☐ You're overthinking this.
☐ Get back up on the horse.
☐ Just give it some time.
☐ It's not the end of the world.
☐ It gets better.
☐ Really, it is.

☐ **TOTALLY OKAY** ☐ **PRETTY OKAY** ☐ **OKAY-ISH**

SIGNATURE MONTH DAY YEAR

"OKAY? OKAY. OKAY!"